Statistics for Marketing and Business

Statistics for Marketing and Business

R. L. GALLOWAY

Stanley Thornes (Publishers) Ltd

First published in 1989 by Hutchinson Education

Reprinted in 1992 by
Stanley Thornes (Publishers) Ltd
Old Station Drive
Leckhampton
CHELTENHAM GL53 0DN

British Library Cataloguing in Publication Data

Galloway, Les
    Statistics for marketing and business.
    1. Statistical mathematics
    I. Title
    519.5

ISBN 0 7487 1058 2

Printed and bound in Great Britain by Scotprint Ltd, Musselburgh.

Dear Student...

With courses becoming more and more intensive there is a greater need for students to have *precise study information* available so that they can study more efficiently and speedily.

At the same time this enables *tutors* to devote more effort towards the understanding and analysis of the subject. Rather than give up valuable time dictating and providing notes, they can concentrate more on actively involving students in the learning process.

In this text the author has covered all aspects of coursework providing:

- A comprehensive text on the subject
- Study and exam tips on each topic
- Self assessment tests
- Past examination questions
- Specimen answers to selected questions
- Answers to self assessment tests

The combination of these elements will greatly improve your confidence and performance in the examinations.

Les Galloway

Contents

General study and exam tips

"In many situations information is so great a part of effectiveness that without information a really clever person cannot get started. With information a much less clever person can get very far." Dr Edward De Bono.

Being successful on a course does not simply result from listening to lectures or reading a textbook. You must become actively involved in the learning process in order to acquire knowledge and skills and perform well in assessments.

There is no reason why you cannot achieve this aim. After all you are on a course of study because an examining authority believes that you have the necessary ability to complete the course successfully. If you are prepared to become actively involved and do the work required, you have every right to feel confident that you can succeed in the final examinations.

These notes are designed to make your study more efficient, to ensure that you use this manual to best advantage and to help you improve both your coursework and your examination techniques. They have been divided into four parts:

1 general study tips
2 improving the quality of your work
3 examination technique
4 studying with this text

■ 1 GENERAL STUDY TIPS

An eminent physicist once said: 'Thinking is 99 per cent perspiration and 1 per cent inspiration'. Take his advice and that of most of us who have had the benefit of a good education. Ignore the advice of those who believe you can prepare yourself for the examination in one or two weeks. Knowledge and skills of any value are not easily learned. For most of us it takes time to understand and permanently remember the content of a subject; instead of forgetting everything immediately the examinations are over. Therefore start working at studying right at the very start of your course and continue at a steady pace until the examinations. Do all the work expected of you by your tutor including homework and mock/mid term examinations. Homework is good practice and the mock exams simulate aspects of the final examination. Doing them as best as you can makes your tutor more willing to help you, as he or she will see that you are playing your part in the learning process.

The knowledge and skills you will gain on your course of study are precisely the kind needed by professional business people. So approach the study of each subject as if you were in real life a business man or woman, or a person following a profession such as accountancy or law. In this way the subject should come alive for you, and your motivation to learn should increase.

To help realise this objective, read a quality daily and Sunday newspaper that has a good business section. By doing this you will discover what is happening on a day-to-day basis and be in a better position to understand the topics you are studying on the course. You will also broaden and deepen your knowledge of the subject. Professional people at work usually read a quality newspaper and monthly or quarterly periodical related directly to their discipline in order to keep abreast of the latest developments. You will probably wish to do the same when you commence work, so why not start now?

Carry a pocket dictionary with you and look up words you hear or read but do not understand. None of us has a complete vocabulary but we can improve it if we really want to be able to read and study more effectively. In the case of students it is even more important because words used in lectures, textbooks or newspapers often become misused in examinations. Some words which cause problems with their meaning or spelling are:

aggregate	disseminate	heterogeneous
antithesis	distinguish	homogeneous
constituents	evaluate	panacea
discipline	facsimile	prognosis

Do you fully understand how these words may be used in the context of your subject? Use a dictionary.

As soon as you start your course, find out if you are going to be given past examination papers for your subject, examiners' reports, specimen answers to previous examination questions and a work scheme. It is probable that they will not all be available at your school, college or university or even from the examining authority. You should, however, obtain as much information about your course of study and the examinations as possible so you know exactly what amount of work lies ahead of you and the academic standard you are expected to reach. This will help in planning your personal workload for the period of your course.

If you do not understand something ask your tutor. Do not assume that you are inadequate because you did not understand something that other students seemed to appreciate. They may be having difficulties too or your lecturer may simply not have explained the point to everyone's satisfaction. If something is overlooked by the tutor, don't be afraid to bring it to his/her attention.

Personal health is something that many students dismiss with comments such as: 'what has health got to do with ability to think?' Studies on the topic have now clearly indicated that general health and mental performance are statistically related. Within four weeks of being given multi vitamin and mineral tablets students in two separate controlled studies improved upon their written performance in intelligence tests by approximately ten points. Your commonsense alone should tell you that you cannot perform at your best if you continually feel tired or have flu or a heavy cold in an examination. Eat a varied diet that includes protein foods, vegetables and fruit, and get some daily exercise even if it is only a good brisk walk home after your day's study.

Contrary to the belief of many students, the best academic work is not done at night-time. Once again research shows that students perform better in the early part of the week, in the daytime – particularly mornings – and in a place where there is natural daylight to read and write by. Therefore plan your study schedule so that it is completed in the day. This will also leave you the evenings and weekends free to relax and enjoy yourself.

■ 2 IMPROVING THE QUALITY OF YOUR WORK

The earlier in the course you bring your work to a satisfactory standard the more likely you are to exhibit a good standard of work in the examinations. Obviously, academic standards do relate to the thinking abilities of the student but they also depend on motivation, and a logical approach to one's work if effective presentation at the appropriate academic standard is to be achieved. Here are three tips that will help you develop a logical approach to the presentation of your work.

Read the question carefully

When undertaking essay or numerical work make sure you read the question very carefully. Underline the key words in the question so that your mind is concentrated on the essential aspects. For example, distinguish between the two main types of question.

DESCRIPTIVE QUESTIONS
A descriptive question is one in which you will be expected to describe or explain something and possibly distinguish it from alternative or similar items or ideas. Two examples are:
(a) *Describe* the *benefits* of *budgetary control* and explain the additional *advantages* of *zero-based* budgeting.
(b) *Explain*, with the *aid of a break-even chart, how the price* of a product *influences* the break-even point.
Some of the key words have been emphasised in italics to give you an idea of which words are at the heart of the question. Always underline or highlight the key words yourself before attempting to answer.

ANALYTICAL QUESTIONS
These include the purely analytical questions, or the analytical question that requires you to evaluate a statement (indicate your level of support for an idea/give it a value) or present your own ideas. Examples of these are:
(a) *Solely analytical:* Analyse the contention that there is no such thing as fixed costs.
(b) *Analytical and evaluative:* How far do you support the idea that adult behaviour is predominantly related to one's early childhood experiences?
If you have been presented with a minicase (short story) or a case study (extended story) detailing opposing opinions regarding a problem a company is faced with, you may be requested to offer your own solution. In this event your answer should analyse the value of all the opinions offered in the case as well as possibly suggesting your own.

Consider also the way a question is structured. If it is in two or more parts give equal time to each if equal marks are awarded to each part. If more marks are awarded to one part than another, allocate your time in the same proportions as the marks awarded. For example, if a question has marks awarded: part (a) 5 marks, part (b) 15 marks (total 20 marks), you should spend a quarter (5/20) of your time answering (a) and three quarters (15/20) on (b).

Sometimes the time you should allocate to a part of a question is indicated by the implied requirements of the question, rather than by marks. For example

Q 1 (a) Briefly outline what you understand by a profit centre.
(b) Give two examples of natural profit centres and two examples of artificial profit centres and explain the effect of the latter motivation.

By using the words 'briefly outline' the examiner is indicating that much less time should be spent on answering part (a). The question requires more marks to be awarded to part (b) as the analytical and applied nature of this part indicates that it is more difficult to answer.

With numerical type questions, such as in accountancy and statistics, do not assume that all you have to do is arrive at the right answer. Your tutor – or an examiner – will expect you to explain what you are doing as you introduce each set of workings, graphs, illustrations or tables. After all, how is your tutor to know how you arrived at the right answer if you do not explain? Even more importantly, even if you give the wrong answer, at least you will be given some marks for those parts of your calculation which are correct. Such subjects involve a large element of communication and if you do not communicate effectively in your answer what you are doing you will lose marks.

Construct an essay plan

Always spend a few minutes constructing an essay plan before answering a question. This only requires jotting down a few notes for each paragraph which indicates the approach you will take to your answer and the points you will include. This will make sure that you construct your essay in a logical manner and that you keep to a target when writing your answer.

Follow up with your tutor

To understand fully what is required when answering questions, ask your tutor about the work you have handed in and had marked if he or she has not commented sufficiently on your script, informing you of where you were right and wrong and why.

■ 3 EXAMINATION TECHNIQUE

If you are studying at college you can start improving your examination technique in the mock/mid term examination which will help you in the coursework assessment during the second half of the course as well as in the final examination. Here are a few tips on improving your presentation.

- *Always do rough workings.* Use essay plans and/or numerical workings to plan your answer, but on a page other than the one on which you start your answer to the question. Cross through your rough working before starting to answer the question.
- Select the questions you intend to answer and *start with the one you think you will find the easiest to answer*. In this way you may gain your highest marks early in the exam which is very important in case you do not complete the examination.
- *Keep an eye on the clock* so that you allow about the same amount of time for answering each question (unless one is a more difficult, compulsory question). Noting the time in order to complete all the questions you are required to answer gives you a better chance of achieving high marks.
- Allow at least a third to half a page for illustrations or diagrams. In this way they look like illustrations rather than scribblings and you have sufficient space available if you have to return to your illustration to add more detail later in the examination. Always explain what your illustration is supposed to illustrate.
- Unless otherwise instructed, use a complete page of graph paper for presenting graphs and make sure that you provide a title for any entries you have made. Explain what your graph illustrates.
- Do not present workings for numerical subjects such as accounts and statistics without explaining what you are doing and why.

If you would like a deeper understanding of study skills and exam techniques a useful book containing a wealth of tips and examples that will help you to succeed in examinations is *How To Pass Exams* by W. G. Leader, also published by Stanley Thornes.

■ 4 STUDYING WITH THIS TEXT

Stanley Thornes' student texts have been specifically designed to act as study aids for students while on a course, as well as present the contents of a subject in a way that is both interesting and informative.

Use this text as part of your study activities, adding your own or your tutor's notes at appropriate points. Study your textbook in great detail, making notes on the chief points in each chapter so that the ideas have gone through your own head and down onto the paper in your own words – though perhaps with key quotations from the text.

Don't get bogged down in any one chapter. If you really can't follow the chapter leave it and go on to the next, returning at a later date. What seems difficult at the start of your course in September will be easier by December and child's play by March! You are going to develop as you do the course – so don't give up too early. Perseverance is everything in acquiring professional status.

Do not just read the specimen answers provided at the end of certain sections. Study their content and structure in the light of what you learned in the particular section and what you learned earlier in this section. In this way your skill in answering questions set by your tutor and/or the examination should improve.

At the end of each section there are examples of past examination questions. Where the answer is to be in essay form jot down beside the question the major points that you think should have been highlighted when answering. Then check back with the appropriate text of the particular section to see if your answer would have been correct. If you are still uncertain, discuss the problem with your tutor.

Talking with the tutor and fellow students is essential for developing the ability to analyse problems.

Always complete the self assessment part of each chapter as they are designed to reinforce what you have learned and improve your recall of the topics. Check your answers with those provided in the manual. As repetition of a process improves one's memory, it is very useful to re-test yourself every few weeks or let someone else read the questions to you and tell you if you got them right.

If the subject covered by the particular manual involves value judgements do not assume that what is mentioned in the manual is the only correct version. Your tutor may have other opinions which are just as valid. What matters is that you have sufficient knowledge of the subject to illustrate a firm understanding of the topic in the examinations.

One of the best ways to study is to buy a lever arch file and make out dividing pages from brown paper for each subject or chapter. File your notes, and your essays and any newspaper cuttings, articles, etc. that are relevant in the appropriate topic position. You will then have an easy to revise and lively set of notes. If you find it a bit bulky to carry, use a ring binder instead and then at the end of every week or two weeks transfer the note you have made to the lever arch file, keeping it at home for safety.

If a particular topic has a suggested project or assignment you may like to try it. You cannot do every project because they are time-consuming – one every six weeks is a good idea and gives you some presentable material for course work assessments, open days, etc.

Now that you have read these Study and Exam Tips you should feel confident to continue with your studies and succeed in the examinations. It just remains for myself and Stanley Thornes to wish you every success on your course.

Introduction

Business statistics is a wide and varied field, but it is primarily concerned with the application of statistical methods to quantitative data in a business context. Many objectives may be served by this approach but, in the main, we are trying to improve efficiency, competitiveness, decision-making and communication.

In general, the practising manager would employ a specialist to apply the appropriate statistical methods to the data under consideration. Such a specialist may be a statistician, an operational researcher or a business analyst. The manager is unlikely to have the time or the expertise to apply the appropriate techniques himself, except in the simplest of cases. However, it is the manager who knows the business, not the statistician, and it is a moot point as to whether it is worse to have the wrong technique badly applied to the right problem, or the right technique correctly applied to the wrong problem.

The manager and the specialist must be able to communicate. The manager has a responsibility to learn enough about the basic principles of statistical methods to enable him to communicate effectively with the specialist, and if he also learns enough to enable him to apply his knowledge to simple situations himself, then so much the better (but one should never lose sight of the proverb 'A little knowledge is a dangerous thing').

This book is intended to address the basic statistical knowledge required by the practising manager. It is not an exhaustive text on the subject, nor even as rigorous as some of my colleagues might like, but is intended to be accessible to the non-specialist. It is designed specifically for those studying for the examinations of such institutions as the Institute of Marketing, the Association of Business Executives and the Institute of Commercial Management, to whom thanks are due for permitting the inclusion of past examination questions, but is likely to be equally suitable for those pursuing other management and professional qualifications (e.g. Diploma in Management Studies), or merely wishing to improve their knowledge.

The book is organised in a logical sequence, but those taking courses may find that topics are taken in a different order. Familiarity with mathematical terminology is helpful but not absolutely essential, and each new concept is dealt with fairly fully on its first appearance. For those who might not be following the book in sequence, the final section of this Introduction outlines the basic mathematical terminology used.

Each topic is illustrated with a worked example, followed by an exercise. It is best to do the exercise before continuing with the chapter, checking that you have got it right. At the end of each chapter is a section on examination technique. Since bad technique is an important cause of failure, this deserves almost as much study as the body of the chapter. Finally, each chapter ends with a multiple choice self-test. These will guide you on the quality of your understanding of the topic.

■ BASIC MATHEMATICS

Mathematical operators

It is assumed that all readers are familiar with basic arithmetic. Knowledge of the following basic operations is assumed:

$+$	add the values on either side of the symbol
$-$	subtract the second value from the first or, if the prefix to a single figure, it indicates a negative value
$\times$	multiply the two values together
$/$	divide the second value into the first
$=$	the expressions on either side have the same value
$>$	the first value is greater than the second value
$<$	the first value is less than the second value
$\geq$	the first value is greater than or equal to the second value
$\leq$	the first value is less than or equal to the second value

Variables and constants

In mathematics we are usually trying to generalise, and avoid using actual numerical values, but the basic principle behind

$$2 + 3 = 5$$

is the same with

$$a + b = c$$

The difference is that in the second example we do not know, or have not yet specified, the numerical values represented by a and b. Letters are usually used to represent such unknown or unspecified values.

Such letters can represent variables or constants. The concept behind this is discussed more fully in Chapter 7, but broadly a variable is unspecified because it can take any of several values, while a constant can take only one value. The price of a loaf of bread is a constant, but the number of loaves we buy is variable.

Variables are usually represented by the letters x, y, z and constants by the letters a, b, c etc.

The letter for a variable may be used to represent any one value of that variable, or all possible values. For example, a general equation for the cost of bread might be:

$$c = ax$$

where c is the total cost, a is the price per loaf and x is the number of loaves.

But we might instead be interested in how many loaves each of the next ten customers buys. Now x can be used to represent all ten numbers of loaves, and individual values are represented by the use of a subscript, thus:

x_2 is the number bought by the second customer
x_i is the number bought by the ith customer

Summation

In statistics we are often dealing with the sum of a number of values x, or even their squares x^2. Rather than say $x_1 + x_2 + x_3 + ...$ we say Σx. This simply means add together all the values of x. (Σ is the Greek letter sigma.)

Powers

We often wish to multiply a value by itself several times. Instead of writing $a \times a \times a$, we write a^3. The superscript represents the number of times the value is to be multiplied, and is usually called a power. This can, of course, be a variable or unspecified constant as in a^x. Occasionally we come across negative powers. This is not the place to explain them: if you do not understand what $x^{-2.5}$ means, do not worry, find a calculator that does.

Order of evaluation

When any mathematical, or arithmetic, expression is evaluated, we do not calculate from left to right. First we calculate anything enclosed by brackets, then we calculate functions (i.e. sine, cosine, logarithm or even Σ), then powers, then multiplication and division and finally addition and subtraction. Only when dealing with equivalent operations do we work from left to right.
Examples:

$$2 + 3 \times 4 - 5 = 2 + 12 - 5 = 9$$
$$(2 + 3) \times 4 - 5 = 5 \times 4 - 5 = 20 - 5 = 15$$

Strictly:

$$2 \times 4/3 \times 6 = 8/3 \times 6 = 2.67 \times 6 = 16$$

not:

$$8/18 = 0.444$$

Where there is any risk of ambiguity, think about the order ($2 \times 4 \times 6/3$ is clear) or use brackets (so is $(2 \times 4)/(3 \times 6)$).

1 | Presenting statistics

◼ 1.1 INTRODUCTION

This book is about the use of quantitative data. We are concerned mainly with its use in commerce, industry and government, but we frequently come across it in private life as well. Indeed, we cannot escape it, so it is in our own interests to be able to understand it, to be able to extract meaning from it, to present it effectively when it can support our case or point of view, to be able to see the shortcomings in other people's presentations.

In this chapter we will be looking at what we mean by statistics, and at ways of presenting quantitative data to assist in communicating the pattern of the data to others, or in understanding it ourselves.

In section 1.2 we will consider what we mean by statistics. In section 1.3 we will look at ways of organising statistics to make their meaning more accessible. In section 1.4 we will look at a number of ways of presenting statistics graphically. In section 1.5 we will consider some of the problems and pitfalls in statistical presentation.

◼ 1.2 WHAT IS A STATISTIC?

The simplest statistic is a single figure which accurately represents something of interest, for instance: I am 173 cm tall; you are twenty-three years old; he takes size eleven shoes.

There are two issues we must consider even with simple statistics like this:

Accuracy How accurate is the statistic? I may in fact be 180 cm tall, and the figure of 173 may be due to poor measurement, or it may be simply untrue. In any exercise involving the use of statistics, we must ensure that our measurements are accurate enough. Excessive accuracy is to be avoided, since this will usually increase the cost, but inadequate accuracy will probably make our results either useless or misleading.

Precision is often confused with accuracy, but has much more to do with how we present the data. It is most unlikely that I am precisely 173 cm tall, and you will only be precisely twenty-three years old for an instant, but these figures are good enough for most purposes. It is of no interest to anyone that I am 173.28576 cm tall. On the other hand, he probably does take precisely size eleven shoes since the nearest possible values of shoe size are ten and twelve. With precision, we are considering how many decimal places we need or, with large numbers, how many significant figures. The precision required will often vary with the use we intend to make of the statistic. For example, if we are speaking in general terms about population issues, it is quite acceptable to talk about the population of China being 1 billion, but if we are trying to work out the rate of change of the population of China then we must have a much more precise figure so that we can compare it with the population last year.

Where we are dealing with a single statistic, then all we are really concerned with is that it should be accurate, or that we should have some idea of its inaccuracy if it is not, and that it should be expressed with an appropriate degree of precision. Too much precision confuses, and is almost as bad as not enough.

■ 1.3 ORGANISING STATISTICS

More often, we are concerned not with a single statistic, but with several, or even several hundred statistics. Let us imagine that we have persuaded the 100 households in a particular street to tell us their annual incomes in £000s. We might obtain a table like Table 1.

Table 1   Incomes of 100 households, £000

12.0	13.2	13.5	12.3	12.4	13.1	13.2	11.5	13.8	13.2
12.5	11.6	14.5	11.8	11.4	9.0	9.9	12.5	12.2	12.1
14.5	9.1	10.2	11.2	13.9	11.8	14.7	13.9	9.1	11.1
10.6	14.1	9.7	9.0	9.7	11.7	14.1	13.5	13.2	9.9
11.8	9.0	9.9	12.2	10.1	10.7	13.1	9.4	9.8	12.9
11.0	14.2	10.3	10.0	12.7	10.1	12.8	8.6	13.9	14.3
13.0	12.2	13.4	9.6	14.3	9.0	11.4	12.7	9.3	11.0
12.4	8.9	14.7	11.4	10.7	14.2	9.4	13.2	9.3	13.7
14.2	10.2	12.1	12.5	11.3	12.6	12.5	11.2	11.2	10.0
12.8	11.1	11.4	13.0	13.8	9.7	10.8	9.7	12.9	13.7

This is not a particularly useful set of statistics as it stands. Any mass of unorganised figures is fairly meaningless, and the first step in any statistical analysis or presentation is the proper organisation of the data. We will probably find the data easier to understand if we were to order it as in Table 2.

Table 2   Incomes of 100 households in ascending order

8.6	9.4	9.9	10.7	11.4	12.0	12.5	13.0	13.5	14.1
8.9	9.4	10.0	10.8	11.4	12.1	12.5	13.0	13.5	14.2
9.0	9.6	10.0	11.0	11.4	12.1	12.5	13.1	13.7	14.2
9.0	9.7	10.1	11.0	11.4	12.2	12.6	13.1	13.7	14.2
9.0	9.7	10.1	11.1	11.5	12.2	12.7	13.2	13.8	14.3
9.0	9.7	10.2	11.1	11.6	12.2	12.7	13.2	13.8	14.3
9.1	9.7	10.2	11.2	11.7	12.3	12.8	13.2	13.9	14.5
9.1	9.8	10.3	11.2	11.8	12.4	12.8	13.2	13.9	14.5
9.3	9.9	10.6	11.2	11.8	12.4	12.9	13.2	13.9	14.7
9.3	9.9	10.7	11.3	11.8	12.5	12.9	13.4	14.1	14.7

We now have a much better picture of income. We can see that it varies between £8.6K and £14.7K, but there is still a lot of information to assimilate. Generally, with large amounts of data, we get a much better picture if we group it.

First, we must decide how many groups, and what range each group should cover. Too many groups would leave us with too much detail to assimilate, while too few groups may obscure detail that is important. The right answer depends on the data we are dealing with and what we wish to obtain from it, but we need to avoid having a large proportion of our data in only one or two groups. It is best if each group is the same size, although this is not always possible as we shall see later.

In this case, we will take seven groups, each covering £1K (Table 3).

Table 3 Incomes of 100 households grouped

Income (£K)	Number
8.0– 8.9	2
9.0– 9.9	19
10.0–10.9	11
11.0–11.9	18
12.0–12.9	20
13.0–13.9	19
14.0–14.9	11

Care must be taken in defining the groups. If we were to say 8.0–9.0, 9.0–10.0 etc., we would not know to which group we should allocate a value of precisely 9.0. Table 3 would be ambiguous and we could end up allocating values to two groups or to none. What we really mean is 8.0–<9.0, 9.0–<10.0 etc., but since we are measuring to a precision of only one decimal place, in this example we can say 8.0–8.9 without ambiguity.

Exercise 1
Now organise the data in Table 2 into four groups of equal range and then into sixteen groups of equal range. Which organisation is best, four, seven or sixteen? Check your answer before going on.

■ 1.4 GRAPHICAL PRESENTATION

Tables are an effective way of presenting statistics if we wish to be able to extract accurate numerical values easily (for instance, how many households have an income of between £11K and £11.9K?). Often we are more interested in seeing the overall pattern of the data and, particularly when trying to communicate with or persuade someone else, a picture carries much more impact and helps to stimulate interest. A table of figures is never interesting, however useful it might be. There are many methods of presenting statistics graphically, and they all have their place. We are going to look at some of the most common methods.

1.4.1 Pictograms

These are in some ways the least useful, but most accessible forms of presentation. The pictogram is a variety of bar chart where the bar is made up of a number of relevant images. The number of the images represents the relative size of whatever is being charted. An example is shown in Fig. 1. The amount of information contained in a pictogram is limited, and while they have an immediate impact they do need to be well presented. A sloppy pictogram will convince no-one.

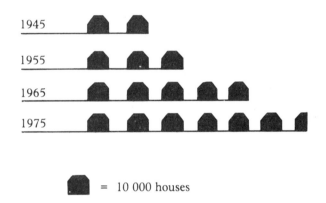

Fig. 1 Number of owner-occupied houses

1.4.2 The histogram

This is the most common, and useful, method of presenting grouped statistics such as the incomes we have been looking at. A histogram of the figures in Table 3 is shown in Fig. 2.

The histogram shows the pattern of the data clearly and gives us a clear indication of the relative importance of the various groups. Strictly, the number in each group is represented by the area, not the height, of the block, so care should be taken to make sure the groups are all of the same size (£1 000 in this case). Sometimes we have some values which are so large or so small compared with the rest that they cannot really be fitted in without distorting the picture. For instance, if the two highest-earning families in our street actually earned £23K and £31K, our histogram would look like Fig. 3.

This distorts the pattern of the bulk of the data and wastes a lot of space without really adding to our understanding. An alternative is to show the average number in the open-ended group >£15K as shown in Fig. 4.

The pattern is much clearer here although we have lost the detailed information

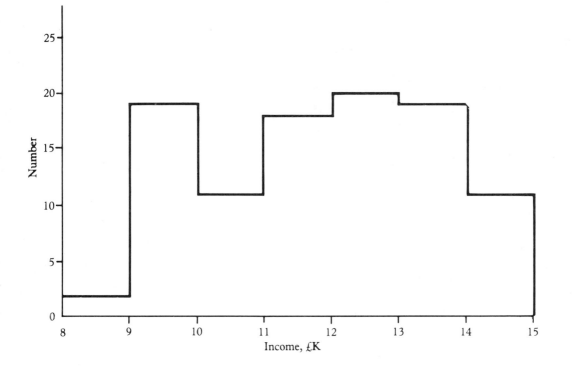

Fig. 2   Incomes of 100 households

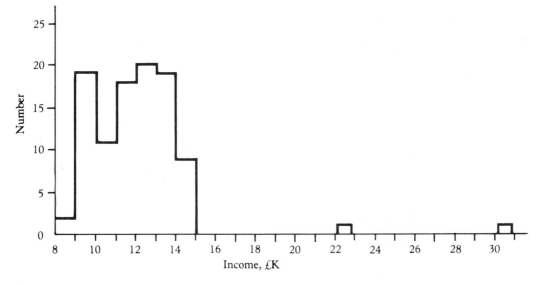

Fig. 3   Incomes of 100 households

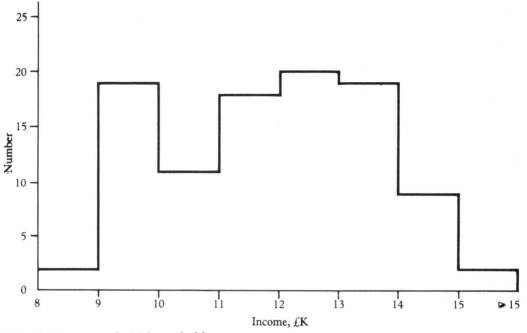

Fig. 4 Incomes of 100 households

about the high incomes. In choosing which approach to use we must strike a balance between clarity of presentation and loss of detail.

Exercise 2
Now plot histograms for the groups you obtained in section 1.3.

1.4.3 The ogive

This alternative method of presenting grouped data is also called the **cumulative frequency distribution**. To produce an ogive of the data in Table 3 we would accumulate a running total in ascending order as shown in Table 4.

Table 4 Incomes of 100 households grouped

Income (£K)	Number	Running total
8.0– 8.9	2	2
9.0– 9.9	19	21
10.0–10.9	11	32
11.0–11.9	18	50
12.0–12.9	20	70
13.0–13.9	19	89
14.0–14.9	11	100

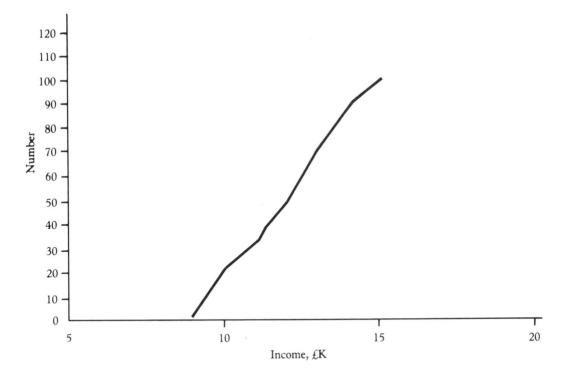

Fig. 5   Incomes of 100 households

We now plot a graph of income against total number, using the top boundaries of the income bands. The result is shown in Fig. 5.

Superficially, the ogive does not appear to give as clear a picture as the histogram, but we shall see in Chapter 2 that it is a very useful method of presenting data in some circumstances.

Exercise 3
Now draw ogives for your grouped data.

When both the axes in an ogive are cumulative percentages, the graph is sometimes called a **Lorenz curve**. The amount by which the curve deviates from a straight line is an indication of the extent to which the distribution of the data is non-uniform.

1.4.4   The frequency polygon

An alternative to the histogram, the frequency polygon, is in effect a histogram with the mid-points of each block joined by a straight line. Figure 6 shows the same data as Fig. 2 plotted as a frequency polygon. It is usually preferred when there are a large number of groups of data.

1.4.5   The bar chart

Superficially, the bar chart looks very similar to the histogram, and the terms are

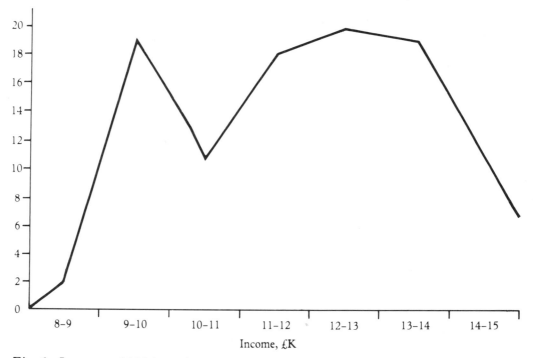

Fig. 6 Incomes of 100 households

frequently used interchangeably. Strictly speaking, the length of the bar is proportional to the value represented in a bar chart, while the area of the bar is proportional to the value in a histogram. Histograms are difficult to use if we have groups of different sizes or, as we have seen, open-ended groups. With the bar chart it does not matter what the various group sizes are. Compare Fig. 7 with Fig. 3.

We can also use bar charts when some of our data is not strictly quantitative. Company X has carried out a survey of its sales turnover by product type and by region. The data is shown in Table 5.

Table 5 Company X sales (£K) by product and region

Region Product	North	South	East	West	Total
A	93	180	50	130	453
B	102	86	50	85	323
C	65	90	120	105	380
D	125	140	135	86	486
E	30	165	75	90	360
Total	415	661	430	496	2002

Figure 8 shows a bar chart of total sales by region.

Exercise 4
Draw a bar chart of total sales by product.

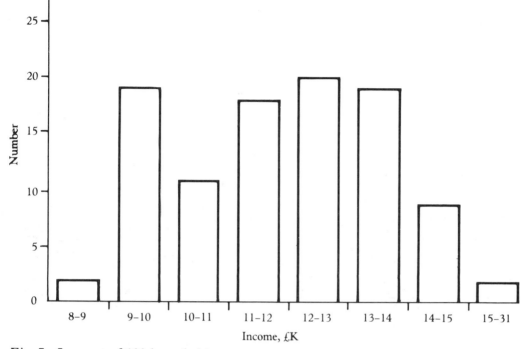
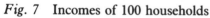

Fig. 7 Incomes of 100 households

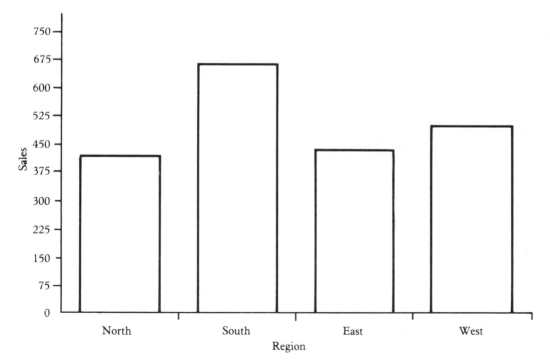

Fig. 8 Company X sales by region

1.4.6 The stacked bar chart

We may wish to show more than just the total sales on our chart. One approach is to present the data as a multiple bar chart as shown in Fig. 9, but this does not show the total.

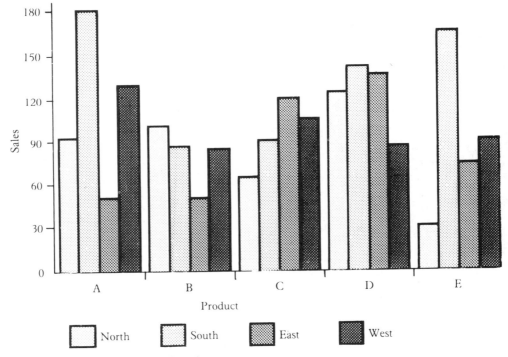

Fig. 9 Sales by product and region

An approach that shows both the individual contributions and the total is the stacked bar chart. Here we start with the bar chart for the North region, but add to this the bar chart for the Southern region and West and East regions so that the total height of the bar is equal to the total sales. Figure 10 shows the same data as Fig. 9 but as a stacked bar chart. You must decide for yourself which is clearer.

Exercise 5
Draw a stacked bar chart showing the total sales by region for Company X.

1.4.7 The pie chart

The pie chart is a useful method of presentation when we are dealing with a few groups or categories which make up a complete unit. It cannot be used in cases which are open-ended, and it is not very satisfactory if there are a large number of categories. It is called a pie chart because we construct a circular pie and divide it into slices according to the relative proportions of the various groups or categories.

The breakdown of the advertising budget for Company X is shown in Table 6.

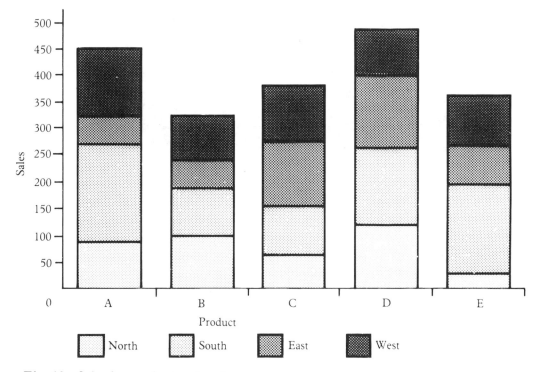

Fig. 10   **Sales by product and region**

Table 6   Company X
advertising budget

Category	Cost (£K)
Posters	8
Newspapers	12
TV	40
Radio	13
Exhibition	15
Total	88

The complete budget is represented here and as there are only a few categories, a pie chart may be used.

First we calculate the value of each category as a proportion of the total, and then we calculate the size of each slice of pie (the angle of the segment it occupies) by multiplying the proportion by 360 (since there are 360 degrees in a circle). Table 7 shows these figures.

If we now draw a circle, we can mark out each segment using a protractor. The result is shown in Fig. 11.

The pie chart is probably the most difficult method of presentation to do well, and it does not actually carry much information. Unlike the histogram or bar chart, it is impossible to read off accurate values. In the correct circumstances the visual impact can be much greater than the other methods. This can be improved by

Table 7   Company X advertising budget

Category	Cost (£K)	Proportion	Angle
Posters	8	0.09	33
Newspapers	12	0.14	49
TV	40	0.45	164
Radio	13	0.15	53
Exhibition	15	0.17	61
Total	88		

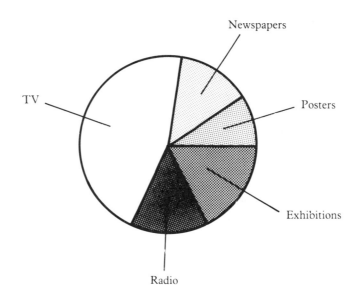

Fig. 11   Company X advertising budget

highlighting the segment under discussion, and the information content can be improved by adding figures. Both of these are illustrated in Fig. 12.

1.4.8   The hi-lo chart

This is a useful form of presentation when we are dealing with a range of values, but are mainly interested in the total range rather than the distribution within that range. Figure 13 shows a hi-lo chart for the share price of Company X over a one-week period. It tells us the maximum and minimum share price on each day, as well as giving a clear picture of any trend.

Such a chart could be used for displaying temperatures in a holiday resort. It would tell us how hot or cold it is likely to get, which is probably more useful than average temperatures would be if we are trying to decide when to take a holiday.

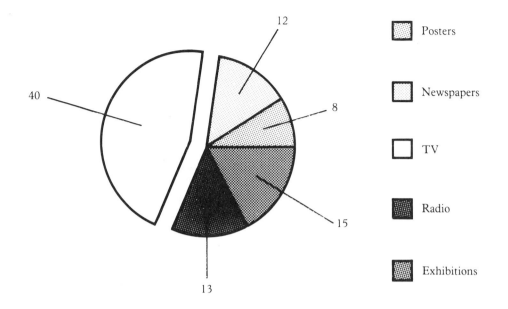

Fig. 12   Company X advertising budget

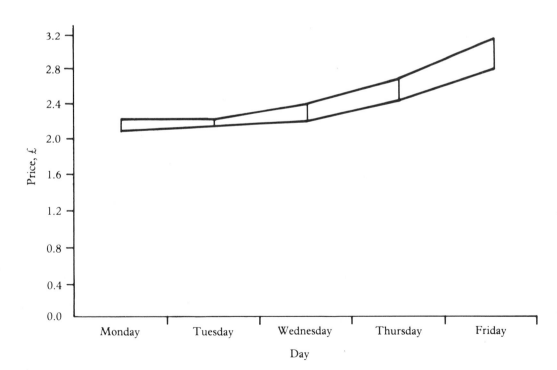

Fig. 13   Company X share price

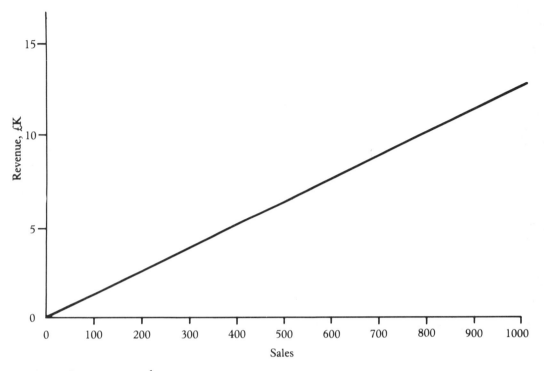

Fig. 14 Revenue v. sales

1.4.9 The Cartesian graph

This particular form of presentation is used most commonly when we are looking at the relationship between two variables. For instance, we might use it to show the relationship between sales volume and sales revenue as in Fig. 14.

It is also frequently used when we wish to suggest that something is changing with time. Figure 15 shows the profit of Company X over the last ten years.

Exercise 6
Draw a Cartesian graph of profit against sales for Company X.

Company X profit and sales revenue (£m)

Year	Profit	Sales
1980	1.30	15.00
1981	1.70	20.00
1982	1.85	27.00
1983	2.40	33.00
1984	3.00	39.00
1985	3.80	42.00
1986	4.90	48.00
1987	6.10	57.00

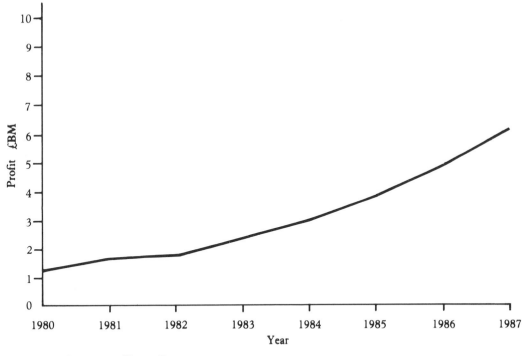

Fig. 15 Company X profit

■ 1.5 PROBLEMS AND PITFALLS

Just as statistics can be presented in such a way as to inform, to maximise the amount of information communicated, so they can also be presented in ways which misinform, which disguise the true importance of the figures, or which simply lose the important information in a mass of unimportant data. This may be done deliberately, because we wish to stress some aspect of the data, or because we wish to divert attention from some aspect of the data, or it may be done accidentally, so that we are simply not using the best method of presentation for our purpose. We are not here concerned with outright dishonesty, though this does arise on occasion.

Figure 16 shows an illustration similar to one used in the early marketing of credit cards in the UK.

It looks very convincing, but if we work out the total income and total expenditure, we find that expenditure exceeds income by £165 over the year. This difference helps make the credit card look more attractive, but is in fact dishonest because we are not comparing like with like.

1.5.1 The false origin

One of the most common ways of manipulating the impact of data is the use of the false origin. The origin of a graph is the point in the bottom left-hand corner where the two axes intersect. It is standard practice to make this the point $x = 0$, $y = 0$,

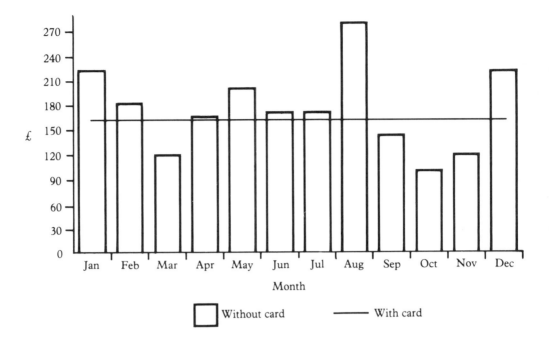

Fig. 16 How a credit card smooths expenditure

although this is less important with *x* than with *y*. Figures 17 and 18 show exactly the same data, Fig. 17 with the true origin of *y* = 0, Fig. 18 with the false origin of *y* = 800.

The impact is considerably greater in Fig. 18, and it is often this initial impact which is most important when presenting statistics, but Fig. 18 is not dishonest since all the data is presented. It can be argued that Fig. 18 is actually to be preferred since in Fig. 17 we are presented largely with blank paper, not information. The false origin is useful when the alternative is a graph composed largely of blank space, but it should be clearly indicated. Figure 19 is acceptable, Fig. 20 is not.

1.5.2 The three-dimensional trick

A common variation on the bar chart uses shapes instead of straight-sided bars. One occasionally sees adverts and company reports using a picture of the company's product. A company producing canned goods may present their turnover figures as shown in Fig. 21, rather than as shown in Fig. 22.

Superficially, this does not seem unreasonable, and it certainly has more impact, but closer consideration shows that the proportions of the can have been kept constant (it would be unrealistic if they were not). This means that a 20 per cent increase in height, which is the scale we are looking at, gives a 73 per cent increase in volume of the can (volume is proportional to the cube of length, and $1.2^3 = 1.728$). Since the eye tends to take volume into account when judging relative sizes,

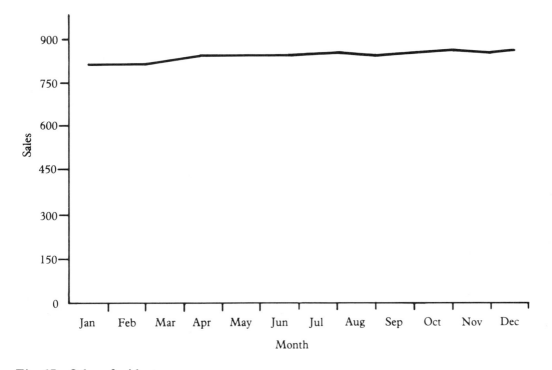
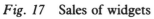

Fig. 17   **Sales of widgets**

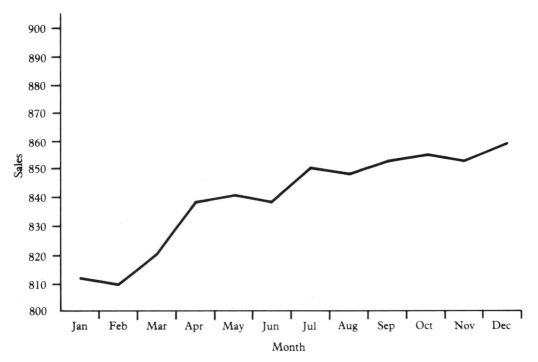

Fig. 18   **Sales of widgets**

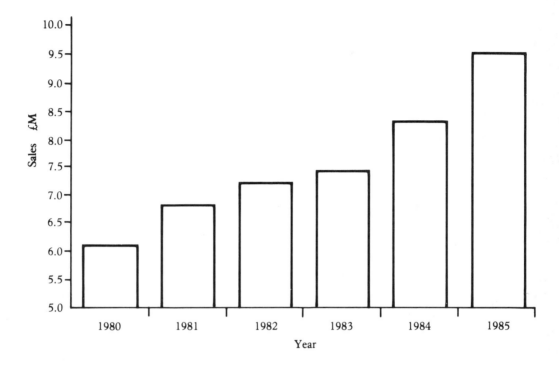

Fig. 19 Annual turnover

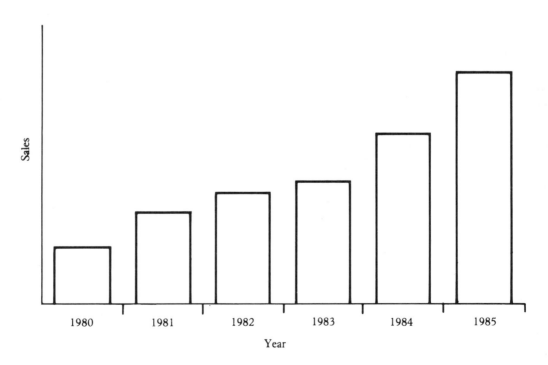

Fig. 20 Annual turnover

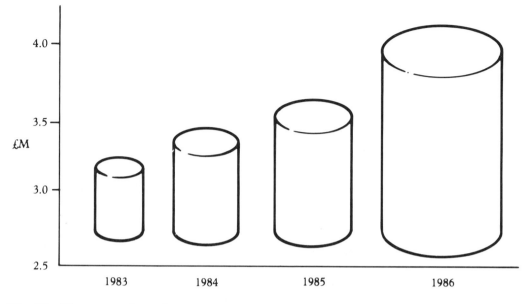

Fig. 21 Turnover of canning company

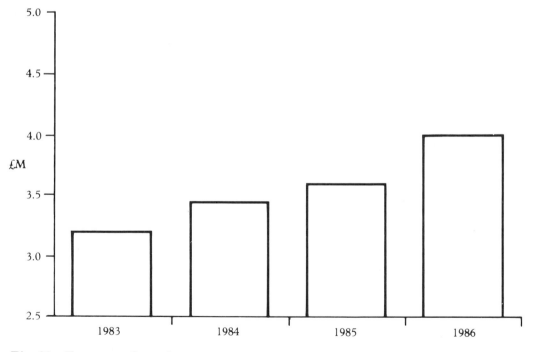

Fig. 22 Turnover of canning company

the effect of this form of presentation is to give an exaggerated impression of growth, and it should therefore be avoided.

1.5.3   Which display is best?

There is, of course, no right answer to this question. The most important elements are the nature of the data, and the audience the display is intended for. The object is to communicate clearly. The display should be clear, uncluttered, easy to read and understand, yet contain all the information necessary. In general, the simpler the display the better: multiple bar charts and layer graphs can contain a large amount of information, but it is often quite difficult to extract. The display chosen should convey its main message at a glance. Elaborate diagrams (e.g. three-dimensional histograms) should be avoided unless you have the facilities necessary to produce a 'professional' image. A well-drawn simple bar chart will command more respect than a more elaborate, but badly drawn display.

Table 8   Which display to use?

	Histogram	Ogive	Frequency polygon	Bar chart
Grouped data	y	y	y	y
Equal groups	y	y	y	y
More than one set of data	n	y		y
Paired values	n	n	n	n
Maximum and minimum values	n	n		
Few groups				

	Stacked bar chart	Pie chart	Hi-lo chart	Cartesian graph
Grouped data	y	y		
Equal groups	y			
More than one set of data	y	n		y
Paired values	n	n	n	y
Maximum and minimum values	n	n	n	
Few groups		y		

y = appropriate
n = not appropriate
  = sometimes appropriate

Table 8 summarises the main types of display that we have considered, and gives broad outlines as to when they might be considered suitable for use.

■ 1.6 SUMMARY

We have learned in this chapter what a statistic is, and how, when faced with a mass of statistics, we might simplify them in order to obtain a clearer picture of the pattern, if any, within them. We have looked at the most frequently used graphical methods of presentation, when their use is appropriate, and some of the ways in which the pattern might be distorted in presentation. In the next chapter we will be looking at ways of extracting useful numerical information from a mass of statistics.

■ 1.7 STUDY AND EXAM TIPS

1 Always use graph paper when drawing graphs, and use a ruler to ensure that lines are straight. Nothing is more annoying to an examiner than a badly drawn sketch scribbled at the side of the page.

2 Do not make the graph too large or too small. If you intend to read values from the graph, it should probably occupy a full page. If it is purely for illustration, then as many as four graphs might be fitted on to one page.

3 Always label graphs clearly. A clear heading or title is essential. The axes should be clearly labelled and scaled, and if there is more than one variable in the graph, each should be labelled. If the examiner has to guess what the graph is about, he may well ignore it altogether.

4 It is rare for a pie chart to be asked for in an exam, but you might take a protractor and pair of compasses with you in case it does arise. If you have to draw a pie chart without the correct equipment, sketch it as best you can and explain the absence of correct equipment in a footnote.

5 Drawing a good graph takes time. Think about the type of graph and the scales to be used on the axes before you start. You will not have time to draw the graph a second time if you get it wrong. Are you sure that the question really requires a graph?

6 Remember that a graph is supposed to communicate information quickly and clearly. Does yours?

■ SELF ASSESSMENT QUESTIONS

Answer the following questions and then check your answers against those at the end of the book. If you get any wrong, re-read the relevant parts of the chapter. If this does not help, then talk to your tutor about the problem.

1 Arranging statistical data in groups helps to extract meaning.
(a) True
(b) False
2 Grouped data is always more accurate.
(a) True
(b) False
3 In which of the following is the length proportional to the value:
(a) Histogram
(b) Bar chart
(c) Ogive
(d) Pie chart
(e) Stacked bar chart?
4 When plotting a histogram, it is important that the groups overlap.
(a) True
(b) False
5 The pie chart is best used when:
(a) There are many groups of values
(b) There are few groups of values
(c) There are open-ended groups

■ EXAMINATION QUESTIONS

Note: Questions frequently cover more than one topic and examples relevant to this chapter will be found at the end of Chapters 2 and 3.

A department store is in the process of preparing its annual report. The marketing manager has assembled the following information about turnover from various departments. You are asked to present this data in a suitable diagram and to draft a report on any significant movements in the turnover.

	Turnover in £000			
Department	1984	1985	1986	1987
Electrical	266	317	325	280
Clothing	85	108	123	156
Furniture	189	176	185	191
Household	92	81	64	53
Total	632	682	697	680

(Institute of Marketing 1988)

Construct accurately on graph paper a simple bar chart and a percentage bar chart to illustrate the following table. Discuss the differing aspects of the table that are highlighted by these two alternative diagrams, including any shortcomings they have in conveying a proper understanding of the data.

(Marks will be given for neatness and visual effectiveness of the diagrams as well as their accuracy.)

Regional distribution of a company's shops in England for the year 1984

London	85
South East	63
South West	24
Midlands	118
North East	10
North West	40

(Institute of Marketing 1986)

A worker was timed (to the nearest minute) on the same repetitive job over a sample period with the following results:

```
30   30   29   30   31   30   31   29   30   30   31   30
31   30   31   28   29   30   30   30   31   30   29   30
30   28   30   29   30   29   29   30   31   30   30   30
30   32   31   32   30   30   30   30   29   31   30   28
30   30
```

(a) Arrange the data into an ungrouped frequency distribution table.
(b) Illustrate with a histogram and a frequency polygon.

(Institute of Commercial Management 1985)

2 │ What is an average?

■ 2.1   INTRODUCTION

Everyone thinks they know what an average is, but we only have to consider the conflicting figures on average earnings claimed by both sides in a pay dispute to wonder if they really are talking about the same thing. In this chapter we will see that, statistically speaking, there are several different 'averages', calculated in different ways to suit different purposes. Strictly speaking, the term average should never be used in statistics because it has no precise meaning. The correct term is **measures of central tendency** which tells us two things about what is commonly called the average:

> There are several different measures
> They are measures of the central or middle value of a set of data

In section 2.2 we will consider some of the situations in which an 'average' may be used. In section 2.3 we will look at the most common average, the **arithmetic mean**. In section 2.4 we will look at the **median**, in section 2.5 the **mode**, and in section 2.6 the **geometric mean**.

■ 2.2   THE USE OF THE AVERAGE

As we saw in Chapter 1, a mass of data such as that shown in Table 9 is not easy to understand or use. It is much easier to handle a single figure, and such a single figure is the 'average'. We probably do not wish to know the 100 individual incomes (particularly if they are anonymous and we cannot relate them to the actual people earning them), but the average income could be used to determine how we ourselves compared with the average, or how the income of this group compared with another group or, indeed, how it compared with the same group last year.

Most commonly when calculating averages we are using them for comparison or for the calculation of other values. For instance, in wages negotiations, a trade union will wish to know the average earnings of its members to compare this with earnings of workers in similar jobs in other firms, while the employer will wish to

Table 9   Incomes of 100 households, £000

12.0	13.2	13.5	12.3	12.4	13.1	13.2	11.5	13.8	13.2
12.5	11.6	14.5	11.8	11.4	9.0	9.9	12.5	12.2	12.1
14.5	9.1	10.2	11.2	13.9	11.8	14.7	13.9	9.1	11.1
10.6	14.1	9.7	9.0	9.7	11.7	14.1	13.5	13.2	9.9
11.8	9.0	9.9	12.2	10.1	10.7	13.1	9.4	9.8	12.9
11.0	14.2	10.3	10.0	12.7	10.1	12.8	8.6	13.9	14.3
13.0	12.2	13.4	9.6	14.3	9.0	11.4	12.7	9.3	11.0
12.4	8.9	14.7	11.4	10.7	14.2	9.4	13.2	9.3	13.7
14.2	10.2	12.1	12.5	11.3	12.6	12.5	11.2	11.2	10.0
12.8	11.1	11.4	13.0	13.8	9.7	10.8	9.7	12.9	13.7

know the average so that it can calculate the cost of any settlement easily (cost = average × number of employees × percentage rise/100).

Knowledge of the average sales for the year will enable a manufacturer to calculate the required production capacity.

Knowledge of the average size of a family will enable a builder to plan the size of house he should build.

Exercise 7
Think of a few other areas where an average might be used.

The average is, of course, not the only statistic we need. The difficulty with any consolidation of data is that we lose detail which might be important. If we only have an average of the data in Table 9, we have lost all information on its shape and range. For this reason the average is rarely used alone, but is generally associated with some measure of the range or **dispersion** of the data. We will look at this in Chapter 3.

■ 2.3   THE ARITHMETIC MEAN

This is without question the most commonly used measure of central tendency, and is usually, but not always, what people mean when they talk about 'average'. It is quite simply the sum of all the values divided by the number of values. Table 10 illustrates its calculation with a simple example.

Table 10   Calculation of the arithmetic mean

Company	Share price
A	103
B	220
C	46
D	58
E	112
F	90
Sum	629

Number of values = 6
Mean = 629/6 = 104.83

Mathematically, we use the Greek letter Σ (pronounced sigma) to denote summation and Σx means add together all the values of the variable x. The formula for the arithmetic mean is therefore:

$$\text{Mean} = \Sigma x/n$$

where n is the number of values of x.

The mean is sometimes denoted by the Greek letter μ (pronounced mew), and sometimes by $\bar{x}$ (called x-bar).

Exercise 8
Calculate the arithmetic mean of the figures in Table 9.

2.3.1 Calculating with grouped data

As you have seen, calculating the mean for a large number of values is tedious and quite easy to get wrong. It is often more convenient to calculate with grouped data, particularly if we have grouped the data already for some other purpose (perhaps to draw a histogram). Table 11 shows the data from Table 9 arranged in groups.

Table 11 Incomes of 100 households grouped

Income (£K)	Number
8.0– 8.9	2
9.0– 9.9	19
10.0–10.9	11
11.0–11.9	18
12.0–12.9	20
13.0–13.9	19
14.0–14.9	11

In order to calculate the mean from this data, we must first find the total value for each group. This is done by finding the mid-point of each group and multiplying it by the number in that group.

Great care needs to be taken in defining the mid-point of the group; we must remember that there are no gaps between groups, however the group range is specified, but we must also take account of any rounding up or down which might have taken place when the data was grouped. In this particular case, a value of 11.94 would have gone into the 11.0–11.9 group, while a value of 11.96 would have gone into the 12.0–12.9 group, so the true group boundaries are at 11.95, 12.95 etc. To find the mid-point we add the true lower boundary to the true upper boundary and divide the result by 2. We then multiply the mid-point by the number in the group, add these totals together and divide the resulting grand total by the number of values we started with. Table 12 shows this.

If you compare this result with that obtained in Exercise 8, you will find that they do not agree (Exercise 8 gave a mean of 11.78). This is an unavoidable consequence of using grouped data. Grouping loses information, and the resulting group totals are at best good estimates of the true totals. We know that in this case

Table 12   Calculation of mean with grouped data

Group	Number	True range	Mid-point	Total in group
8.0– 8.9	2	7.95– 8.95	8.45	16.90
9.0– 9.9	19	8.95– 9.95	9.45	179.55
10.0–10.9	11	9.95–10.95	10.45	114.95
11.0–11.9	18	10.95–11.95	11.45	206.10
12.0–12.9	20	11.95–12.95	12.45	249.00
13.0–13.9	19	12.95–13.95	13.45	255.55
14.0–14.9	11	13.95–14.95	14.45	158.95
Sum	100			1181.00
Mean	1181/100			11.81

the two values in the first group are 8.6 and 8.9, so that the true group total is 17.5. The figure we used was 16.9. We must accept that if we group data for convenience, or to simplify calculation, then we sacrifice some accuracy in the process. If we cannot afford any loss of accuracy, then we must work with the original figures.

The formula for the mean using grouped data is:

$$\mu = \frac{\Sigma n_i x_i}{\Sigma n_i}$$

where x_i is the mid-point of group i and n_i is the number in that group.

Working with open-ended groups poses special problems. If our first group had simply said ≤8.9, we would have no way of establishing a lower limit for the group (although in this particular case it could not be less than 0). There are a number of fairly complex methods available for estimating the mid-points of open groups, but they are of doubtful value, and beyond the scope of this book. The best approach is to avoid open groups if you intend to calculate with the data.

Exercise 9
You have monitored the performance of sixty-seven workers over one shift, and have obtained the following data on number of defectives produced. Calculate the arithmetic mean number of defectives per worker.

Defects	Number of workers
0– 2	5
3– 5	7
6– 8	6
9–11	5
12–14	4
15–17	10
18–20	11
21–23	9
24–26	6
27–29	4

2.3.2 Using the arithmetic mean

The arithmetic mean is particularly useful among measurements of central tendency in that it allows some of the original data to be reconstructed. We can recalculate the total from the mean and the number of observations, or we can calculate totals for different numbers. For example, if one machine can produce at a mean rate of 30 widgets per hour, then ten machines can produce 300 and thirty machines 900 widgets per hour. Likewise, effects of changes in the mean can be calculated. If our mean rate of production increases by 5 widgets per hour, then, with ten machines, our total capacity increases to 350 widgets per hour. This may seem obvious, but the possibility of calculating with the mean does not arise with the other measures of central tendency.

The arithmetic mean does have some drawbacks. If we consider the average size of family mentioned earlier, we may well find that the mean family size is say 3.78. This has all the properties of the arithmetic mean as Exercise 10 shows:

Exercise 10
Given that the mean family size is 3.78:

What is the total population of a town of 40 000 families?
How many dwellings would be required to house 120 000 people?

---

but we do not know how big these dwellings should be because we do not know the size of any of the families in question. We could have seventy families of 2 people and thirty of 8, and still get a mean of 3.78. The only thing we can say with confidence is that no family will contain 3.78 people. In other words, the arithmetic mean describes the population as a whole, but does not describe individual members of that population.

Another drawback of the arithmetic mean is that large values tend to distort it. If one of our 100 households in Table 9 belonged to a millionaire industrialist who, for whatever reason, had chosen to live in the same street as the rest of us, and had an income of £650K per year, then the mean income would become £18.14K. Now not only does no household have this precise income, but apart from our eccentric millionaire, nobody earns this much, and our 100 householders would rightly dismiss it as meaningless. It is this property of the arithmetic mean which often leads to conflict over the starting point in wage negotiations. If a few high-earners raise the mean to the point where most of the workforce are earning less than the mean, the union side will then often refuse to accept this figure as a true reflection of the income of their members.

■ 2.4 THE MEDIAN

The median is a measure of central tendency which overcomes some of the shortcomings of the arithmetic mean. It is simply defined as the middle value. In other words, 50 per cent of our population are below the median and 50 per cent above. It cannot be calculated, but has to be counted, which means that the data must first be put into rank order. Table 13 shows the data from Table 9 in ascending order.

Table 13 Incomes of 100 households in ascending order

8.6	9.4	9.9	10.7	11.4	12.0	12.5	13.0	13.5	14.1
8.9	9.4	10.0	10.8	11.4	12.1	12.5	13.0	13.5	14.2
9.0	9.6	10.0	11.0	11.4	12.1	12.5	13.1	13.7	14.2
9.0	9.7	10.1	11.0	11.4	12.2	12.6	13.1	13.7	14.2
9.0	9.7	10.1	11.1	11.5	12.2	12.7	13.2	13.8	14.3
9.0	9.7	10.2	11.1	11.6	12.2	12.7	13.2	13.8	14.3
9.1	9.7	10.2	11.2	11.7	12.3	12.8	13.2	13.9	14.5
9.1	9.8	10.3	11.2	11.8	12.4	12.8	13.2	13.9	14.5
9.3	9.9	10.6	11.2	11.8	12.4	12.9	13.2	13.9	14.7
9.3	9.9	10.7	11.3	11.8	12.5	12.9	13.4	14.1	14.7

Counting from the lowest, we find that the 50th value is 11.8 and the 51st 12.0. The mid-point of these is 11.9 and that is our median. (Where there is an odd number of values, the median is the value of the middle item; with an even number, as here, the median lies between the two midmost values.)

2.4.1 Calculating from grouped data

Medians can be calculated for grouped data, the procedure being as follows.

First calculate the cumulative total. This is shown in Table 14 for data based upon that in Table 11.

Table 14 Incomes of 100 households grouped

Income (£K)	Number	Cumulative total
8.0– 8.9	2	2
9.0– 9.9	19	21
10.0–10.9	11	32
11.0–11.9	21	53
12.0–12.9	17	70
13.0–13.9	19	89
14.0–14.9	11	100

Now identify the group containing the mid-point. In this case it is halfway between item 50 and 51 which is in the group 11.0–11.9.

We now find the median by proportion. There are 21 items in the group and the median lies between items 18 and 19 (we identify item 18 by subtracting the cumulative total at the previous group from 50).

The actual median value is

$$S + M \times W/N$$

where S is the starting value of the group, M is the number in the group of the median, W is the group width and N is the number of items in the group.

In this case we have

$$\text{Median} = 10.95 + 18.5 \times 1/21 = 11.83$$

2.4.2 Reading from an ogive

Whether we have grouped data or not, the easiest way to find the median is to read it off an ogive. We simply draw a horizontal line from the 50 per cent point on the y axis and read off the median from the x axis. Figure 23 illustrates this with the ogive used in Chapter 1.

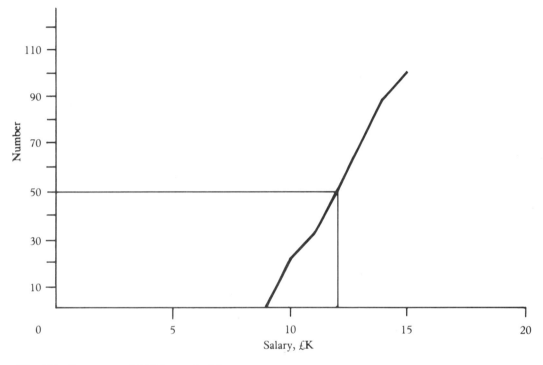

Fig. 23 Incomes of 100 households

Exercise 11
Find the median for the data in Exercise 9.

2.4.3 Using the median

The median cannot be used in calculation. We cannot say that if the median salary is £10 000 the salary bill for 100 employees will be £1 000 000. The salary of one employee alone could be £1 000 000. The median is the mid-point, and this is frequently seen as the fairest basis for comparison, but it does not contain any information on the magnitude of other values in the data. It is generally used in such things as salary surveys, because most people wish to know how they compare with the generality, not how they compare with the exception such as our eccentric millionaire. If you are earning less than the median, then you know that more than 50 per cent of the population are earning more than you and you may feel entitled to be resentful. If you are earning less than the mean, you may, as we have seen, still be the second highest earner. The median is frequently used by the trade-union side in wage negotiations, hence the lack of agreement about the starting point.

■ 2.5 THE MODE

This is perhaps the most obvious measure of central tendency. It is quite simply the most commonly occurring value or, with grouped data, the group containing the largest number of items. It can only be obtained by counting. If we look at Table 13 we will find that the most common value is 13.2 which occurs five times, next come 9.0, 9.7, 11.4 and 12.5 which all occur four times. It is fairly obvious that we may not always have a single mode. There is nothing to prevent there being five 9.0s in the data, and had this arisen we would have had modes of 9.0 and 13.2.

The modal group for this data is 12.0–12.9 with twenty items (see Table 12).

This is the sort of measure of central tendency our builder requires when asking for average family size. If, as is likely, the modal family size is four (parents and two children) then he would be well advised to build three-bedroomed houses.

Never look at the mode in isolation. Always consider whether it represents a significant part of the total. For instance, if 50 per cent of families have four members (the mode represents 50 per cent of the population), then the four-member family is important compared with others. Only 5 per cent of our population earned £13.2K and are therefore, by themselves, relatively unimportant. The mode is most useful when it represents a significant proportion of the total population.

■ 2.6 THE GEOMETRIC MEAN

So important is the arithmetic mean that it is frequently referred to simply as the mean. However, it is only one of several different means. The next most important is the geometric mean.

The geometric mean of n values is the nth root of the product of the n values. Expressed mathematically:

$$\text{Geometric mean} = \sqrt[n]{(X_1 \times X_2 \times X_3 \times X_4 \times X_5 \ldots \times X_n)}$$

It is of limited use, and we do not need to spend much time on it. It is principally used when we are concerned with percentage changes in data, while the arithmetic mean is more suitable where we are concerned with the actual value of the change.

Exercise 12
The share prices, in pence, of six companies are as follows.
Calculate the geometric mean share price.

103	*220*	*46*	*58*	*112*	*90*

■ 2.7 SUMMARY

In this chapter we have looked at the idea of the measure of central tendency (or average) as a means of reducing a mass of data to one single useful value. We have seen that the particular value of use depends upon the precise application we have in mind, and how the use of the 'wrong' average can give rise to error and misunderstanding. We have identified four of the most common measures of central tendency, their calculation, and the circumstances in which they are most useful.

In the next chapter we will go on to look at a second statistic which is an essential companion of the measure of central tendency, the measure of dispersion.

■ 2.8 STUDY AND EXAM TIPS

1 Pay particular attention to the measure of central tendency that the question requires. If the question specifies the mean, then it will require the arithmetic mean. If the question simply says 'average', or simply implies that some measure of central tendency is required, then you must decide for yourself whether mean, median or mode is most appropriate.

2 Tell the examiner which you are calculating and why.

3 If you are using a graphical method to determine the median or mode, then remember the tips about graphs in Chapter 1, they are all relevant.

4 You are unlikely to be asked to calculate a mean for a large volume of data, or to find a median or mode for a very small amount of data. If the question seems to be asking you to calculate the mean of 50 values (or the median or mode of 5). think again about whether this is the correct statistic for the situation.

■ SELF ASSESSMENT QUESTIONS

Answer the following questions and then check your answers against those at the end of the book. If you get any wrong, re-read the relevant parts of the chapter. If this does not help, then talk to your tutor about the problem.

1 The median is:
(a) The most common value
(b) The middle value

(c) The value of the middle observation

2 Which is the best measure of central tendency for the following:

(a) People's height

(b) Weights of bags of sugar

(c) Salaries

(d) People's shoe size

(e) Yield per acre of wheat in farming

(f) Number of defectives per batch in manufacturing?

3 What is the mode of the following data:
   15, 24, 13, 12, 14, 15, 9, 18, 15, 14, 10?

4 The original total can be reconstructed from the:

(a) Median

(b) Mean

(c) Mode

(d) None of these

■ EXAMINATION QUESTIONS

It is rare for an examination question to be concerned about central tendency but not about dispersion. A selection of relevant questions will be found at the end of Chapter 3.

3 | Measures of dispersion

■ 3.1 INTRODUCTION

In Chapter 2 we looked at a number of ways of identifying the central tendency, or average, of a set of data. While this is probably the most important statistic, we are usually equally interested in the way in which the values vary about this average, in other words, the **dispersion** of the data. We need to know whether the individual values are likely to be closely clustered around the average, or whether they are likely to be widely dispersed. For instance, if we are looking at a machine for packing sugar, we may know that it can be set to give a mean weight of 1 kilogram (1 kg) but it is obviously important to know whether this weight will vary between say 0.99 kg and 1.01 kg, or between 0.9 kg and 1.1 kg.

Just as there are several measures of central tendency, there are several measures of dispersion, and in this chapter we will look at some of the most important.

In section 3.2 we will look at the **range**, in section 3.3 at **quartiles**, in section 3.4 at the **mean absolute deviation**, in section 3.5 at the **standard deviation**, and in section 3.6 at **skewness**.

■ 3.2 THE RANGE

The range is the simplest of all measures of dispersion and takes two forms. One is simply a statement of the maximum and minimum values, while the other is a numerical measure of the difference between the maximum and minimum values.

If we look at the data in Table 15, it is quite obvious that the range is 8.6 to 14.7

Table 15 Incomes of 100 households in ascending order

8.6	9.4	9.9	10.7	11.4	12.0	12.5	13.0	13.5	14.1
8.9	9.4	10.0	10.8	11.4	12.1	12.5	13.0	13.5	14.2
9.0	9.6	10.0	11.0	11.4	12.1	12.5	13.1	13.7	14.2
9.0	9.7	10.1	11.0	11.4	12.2	12.6	13.1	13.7	14.2
9.0	9.7	10.1	11.1	11.5	12.2	12.7	13.2	13.8	14.3
9.0	9.7	10.2	11.1	11.6	12.2	12.7	13.2	13.8	14.3
9.1	9.7	10.2	11.2	11.7	12.3	12.8	13.2	13.9	14.5
9.1	9.8	10.3	11.2	11.8	12.4	12.8	13.2	13.9	14.5
9.3	9.9	10.6	11.2	11.8	12.4	12.9	13.2	13.9	14.7
9.3	9.9	10.7	11.3	11.8	12.5	12.9	13.4	14.1	14.7

or 6.1, depending on which form we require. It is easier to identify the range when the data has been ranked, but that is really all there is to it.

The range is not a particularly useful measure, but it does tell us the largest and smallest values we need to allow for. It is the measure of dispersion which best matches the mode as a measure of central tendency.

◼ 3.3 QUARTILES

Quartiles are one of a whole family of '-iles', and we can have as many or as few as we require (and as the data justifies). The lower quartile is that value below which one-quarter, or 25 per cent, of our data lies, while the upper quartile is that value above which 25 per cent of our data lies. The quartile thus matches the median as a measure of central tendency.

Quartiles are calculated in exactly the same way as the median. If we look at the data in Table 15 we see that the 25th value is 10.1, and the 26th 10.2, so 25 per cent of the values lie below 10.15 which is the lower quartile. Similarly, the upper quartile lies between the 74th and 75th items at 13.15.

The quartiles provide rather more information on the way in which the values vary than does the range, and we can provide more information still by looking at smaller divisions. For instance, we could consider the **octiles**, where the data is divided into eight groups, each containing 12.5 per cent of the values, or **deciles** where each group contains 10 per cent of the values, or even **centiles** where we have groups containing 1 per cent of the values (in the case of the data in Table 15, each value is a centile so we are back to the original data).

Since the whole object of calculating measures of central tendency and dispersion is to reduce the number of figures we have to deal with to something manageable, it is rare for us to go beyond deciles.

By far the easiest way to calculate -iles is to read them off an ogive, and Figure 24 shows the median and octiles for the data in Table 15.

Quartiles and their associated measures are most suitable for making detailed comparisons as, for example, in salary surveys. A rarely used variation on the quartile is the **quartile deviation** which is, in effect, the mean difference between the quartiles and the median. It is found by subtracting the lower quartile from the upper quartile and dividing the result by two.

◼ 3.4 THE MEAN ABSOLUTE DEVIATION

If we wish to obtain a mathematical measure of the variation of values about the mean, it seems fairly logical that we should determine the deviation of each value from the mean and then find the mean of these deviations. As Table 16 shows, this does not work since the positive and negative values cancel each other.

A way of overcoming this problem is to ignore the sign of the deviation or, in mathematical terms, to use the **absolute** value (an absolute value is one which is neither positive nor negative). If we do this we get the result shown in Table 17.

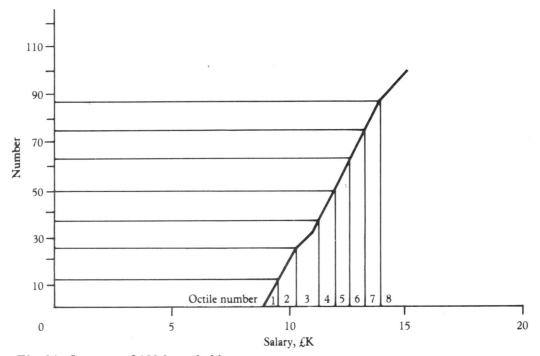

Fig. 24 Incomes of 100 households

This is a fairly easily calculated statistic, which tells us a certain amount about the variation of data about the (arithmetic) mean, but it is of limited use statistically, and is generally considered to be a simple, but inferior, substitute for the standard deviation which we will consider in the next section.

Exercise 13
Calculate the mean absolute deviation of the following data:

Incomes of 30 households, £000

12.0	*13.2*	*13.5*	*12.3*	*12.4*	*13.1*	*13.2*	*11.5*	*13.8*	*13.2*
12.5	*11.6*	*14.5*	*11.8*	*11.4*	*9.0*	*9.9*	*12.5*	*12.2*	*12.1*
14.5	*9.1*	*10.2*	*11.2*	*13.9*	*11.8*	*14.7*	*13.9*	*9.1*	*11.1*

Table 16   Calculation of the mean deviation

Company	Share price	Deviation (price − 104.83)
A	103	−1.83
B	220	115.17
C	46	−58.83
D	58	−46.83
E	112	7.17
F	90	−14.83
Sum	629	0.00

Number of values = 6
Mean = 629/6 = 104.83

Table 17   Calculation of the mean absolute deviation

Company	Share price	Absolute deviation
A	103	1.83
B	220	115.17
C	46	58.83
D	58	46.83
E	112	7.17
F	90	14.83
Sum	629	244.66

Mean absolute deviation (MAD) = 244.66/6 = 40.78

◼ 3.5   THE STANDARD DEVIATION

The mean absolute deviation is fine as far as it goes, but it is not particularly satisfactory simply to ignore negative values because they are inconvenient. A more legitimate approach is to square the values. This eliminates negatives mathematically, since a negative number squared gives a positive number. More importantly, as we will see in future chapters, it gives us a measure of dispersion of great usefulness.

If we look at the data in Table 16 again, we now square each deviation of share price from the mean as shown in Table 18.

If we now divide this sum by the number of values (6) we get 3 198.8051. The problem we now face is what are these 3 198? Since we started with share prices (in pence) and squared them, these must be square pence, which is a fairly nonsensical unit of measurement. In order to convert this measure of dispersion back into usable units we must take the square root, which in this case is 56.558. In other words, the standard deviation of share price is 56.558 pence.

The standard deviation is often represented by the Greek letter σ (called sigma). The square of the standard deviation which we first calculated is sometimes referred to as the **mean squared deviation**, and sometimes as the **variance**.

Mathematically we can express the standard deviation as:

$$\sigma = \sqrt{\frac{\Sigma(x - \bar{x})^2}{n}}$$

Where $\bar{x}$ is the mean of all the values of x, and n is the number of values of x.

Table 18   Calculation of the standard deviation

Company	Share price	Deviation	Deviation squared
A	103	−1.83	3.3489
B	220	115.17	13 264.128
C	46	58.83	3 460.9689
D	58	46.83	2 193.0489
E	112	7.17	51.4089
F	90	−14.83	219.9289
Sum			19 192.831

This formula is fairly tedious to calculate with, and a rather simpler one is:

$$\sigma = \sqrt{(\Sigma x^2/n - \bar{x}^2)}$$

Table 19 shows the calculation of the standard deviation of share pricing using this approach.

Table 19   Calculation of the standard deviation

Company	Share price	Share price squared
A	103	10 609
B	220	48 400
C	46	2 116
D	58	3 364
E	112	12 544
F	90	8 100
Sum		85 133

$$\sigma = \sqrt{(85\ 133/6 - 104.83^2)}$$
$$\text{or } \sigma = \sqrt{(14\ 188.833 - 10\ 989.328)}$$
$$= \sqrt{3199.505}$$
$$= 56.5642$$

The small difference between these two methods (the first method gave 56.558) is due entirely to the limitations of calculators.

Note: If you use a calculator, or computer program, which has a standard deviation function built in, you may find that it uses $n-1$ rather than n in its calculation (some give you the option of n or $n-1$). We will be looking at the reason for this in Chapter 8; meanwhile, use n not $n-1$.

Exercise 14
Calculate the standard deviation of the following data:

Incomes of 30 households, £000

12.0	13.2	13.5	12.3	12.4	13.1	13.2	11.5	13.8	13.2
12.5	11.6	14.5	11.8	11.4	9.0	9.9	12.5	12.2	12.1
14.5	9.1	10.2	11.2	13.9	11.8	14.7	13.9	9.1	11.1

3.5.1   Calculating with grouped data

As we found with the mean in Chapter 2, calculating with a large number of values is tedious, and quite easy to get wrong. It is often more convenient to calculate with grouped data, particularly if we have grouped it already for some other purpose (perhaps to draw a histogram). Table 20 shows the data from Table 15 arranged in groups.

In order to calculate the standard deviation from this data, we must first find the mean. You should refer to Chapter 2 for the details of how this was done. We also need the mid-point of each group and the same care needs to be taken in defining it as we took in calculating the mean. Table 21 shows the mid-points.

Table 20 Incomes of 100 households grouped

Income (£K)	Number
8.0– 8.9	2
9.0– 9.9	19
10.0–10.9	11
11.0–11.9	18
12.0–12.9	20
13.0–13.9	19
14.0–14.9	11

Table 21 Calculation of standard deviation with grouped data

Group	Number	True range	Mid-point
8.0– 8.9	2	7.95– 8.95	8.45
9.0– 9.9	19	8.95– 9.95	9.45
10.0–10.9	11	9.95–10.95	10.45
11.0–11.9	18	10.95–11.95	11.45
12.0–12.9	20	11.95–12.95	12.45
13.0–13.9	19	12.95–13.95	13.45
14.0–14.9	11	13.95–14.95	14.45

We can now calculate the total sum of squares (Σx^2) by squaring each mid-point and multiplying by the number in the group. This is shown in Table 22.

Table 22 Calculation of standard deviation with grouped data

Group	Number	Mid-point	Square of mid-point	Square × number
8.0– 8.9	2	8.45	71.4025	142.805
9.0– 9.9	19	9.45	89.3025	1 696.7475
10.0–10.9	11	10.45	109.2025	1 201.2275
11.0–11.9	18	11.45	131.1025	2 359.845
12.0–12.9	20	12.45	155.0025	3 100.05
13.0–13.9	19	13.45	180.9025	3 437.1475
14.0–14.9	11	14.45	208.8025	2 296.8725
Sum	100			14 234.649

We know that the mean is 11.81 so we can now calculate the standard deviation from the equation:

$$\sigma = \sqrt{(\Sigma x^2/n - \bar{x}^2)}$$

and we get:

$$\sigma = \sqrt{(14\,234.649/100 - 11.81^2)}$$
$$= \sqrt{(142.34649 - 139.4761)}$$
$$= \sqrt{2.87039}$$
$$= 1.6942$$

The formula for the standard deviation with grouped data is:

$$\sigma = \sqrt{(\Sigma(n_i x_i^2)/\Sigma n_i - \bar{x}^2)}$$

where x_i is the mid-point of the group i, and n_i is the number in that group.

As with the mean, calculating the standard deviation with grouped data does lead to some loss of accuracy, and if this is unacceptable, the original data must be used.

Exercise 15
You have monitored the performance of sixty-three workers over one shift, and have obtained the following data on number of defectives produced. Calculate the standard deviation of the number of defectives per worker.

Defects	Number of workers
0– 2	5
3– 5	7
6– 8	6
9–11	5
12–14	4
15–17	10
18–20	11
21–23	9
24–26	6
27–29	4

■ 3.6 SKEWNESS

Not all data is distributed symmetrically about the mean, and we occasionally require some measure of the skewness of the distribution of data that we are dealing with. When data is distributed symmetrically, the mean, median and mode are all equal. When the mean is greater than the median and mode, the distribution is said to be positively skewed, and when the mean is less than the median and mode, it is negatively skewed. The most common measure of skewness is **Pearson's coefficient of skewness**, which is:

$$\frac{(\text{Mean} - \text{mode})}{\text{Standard deviation}}$$

Since the mode is not always readily available, or even clearly identifiable, an alternative formula is:

$$\frac{3(\text{Mean} - \text{median})}{\text{Standard deviation}}$$

■ 3.7 SUMMARY

In this chapter we have looked at four different measures of the dispersion of a set of data, we have considered how they are calculated and, in the case of the range and the quartiles, how they might be used. We have not looked at the use of the most important measure, the standard deviation, to any great extent because a proper understanding of its use requires a knowledge of **probability** and **statistical distributions** which we will cover in Chapters 4 and 5. We will, in fact, make extensive use of the standard deviation throughout the rest of the book.

■ 3.8 STUDY AND EXAM TIPS

1 The measure of dispersion goes with the measure of central tendency. If you are dealing with means, then you will be considering mean absolute deviations, or standard deviations. The '-iles' go with the median and the range with the mode.

2 The '-iles' are almost always best read from a graph.

3 Take particular care when calculating standard deviations. Any calculation which requires you to subtract one previously calculated figure from another requires care since small errors in the original calculations can have a disproportionate effect on the final difference. If you find that $\Sigma x^2/n$ is less than $\bar{x}^2$, then you have obviously gone wrong somewhere (you cannot take a square root of a negative number). If you cannot find the mistake and correct it in the time available, make a note for the examiner saying that you do know that the result is impossible.

■ SELF ASSESSMENT QUESTIONS

Answer the following questions and then check your answers against those at the end of the book. If you get any wrong, re-read the relevant parts of the chapter. If this does not help, then talk to your tutor about the problem.

1 What is the range of the following data:
  15, 24, 13, 12, 14, 15, 9, 18, 15, 14, 10?

2 Quartiles divide data up into how many equal parts:
(a) 2
(b) 8
(c) 4?

3 An absolute value is:
(a) Always the same
(b) Always positive
(c) Always negative
(d) Neither positive nor negative
4 The standard deviation is:
(a) The mean of the squares minus the square of the mean
(b) The square root of (a)
(c) The square root of the MAD
(d) The square root of the mean squared deviation
5 As a measure of dispersion, quartiles usually go with:
(a) The mode
(b) The geometric mean
(c) The median

■ EXAMINATION QUESTIONS

Displayed below is the value of eighty-four consecutive orders received by a sales department and rounded down to the nearest pound.
   (a) Arrange the data in a suitable grouped frequency table. (4 marks)
   (b) Calculate the arithmetic mean first using the original data and second using your grouped table. Explain the difference that is found between these two results. (8 marks)
   (c) Calculate also the coefficient of variation from the grouped table and explain its interpretation. (8 marks)

43	2	56	63	22	7	30	72	16	40	55	8	31	23
92	15	77	6	70	44	88	14	58	39	18	42	101	7
11	104	22	98	17	115	19	61	3	23	95	4	33	82
69	35	109	12	53	25	36	32	40	79	16	114	45	10
23	41	18	51	43	5	102	17	118	28	59	48	19	107
40	64	9	37	84	57	21	74	39	6	87	18	67	29

(Institute of Marketing 1988)

A company's weekly turnover is recorded over a period of 120 weeks in the following frequency table:

Turnover (£000)	No. of weeks
<50	2
50 and <70	5
70 and <90	9
90 and <110	14
110 and <130	18
130 and <150	23
150 and <170	36
170 and <190	13

(a) Construct a histogram for the distribution. (5 marks)
(b) Calculate the arithmetic mean and standard deviation. (10 marks)
(c) What are the implications to the company of (a) and (b)? (5 marks)

(Institute of Marketing 1987)

The weekly earnings of employees in a large catering establishment are compared with those in an engineering company in the table below:

	No. of employees	
Weekly earnings (£)	*Catering*	*Engineering*
80 but <100	20	10
100 but <120	56	18
120 but <135	71	39
135 but <150	45	46
150 but <165	17	42
165 but <180	12	33
180 but <210	8	25
210 but <240	3	11

(a) Construct a cumulative frequency curve (ogive) for each of the two sectors of employment. (8 marks)

(b) Hence, or otherwise, estimate the value of the median and the quartile deviation for each of the two groups of employees and compare the results of their weekly earnings. (12 marks)

(Institute of Marketing 1987)

The following table shows the distribution of weekly earnings in a business:

£ per week	*No. of workers*
<60	5
60 and <80	120
80 and <100	245
100 and <120	520
120 and <140	395
140 and <160	330
160 and <180	235
180 and <200	103
200 and over	27

Calculate the median, the lower and upper quartiles, the inter-quartile range and the quartile deviation.

(Institute of Commercial Management 1985)

The following table was extracted from a company's payroll showing the distribution of weekly earnings among the factory operatives for 1984:

Weekly earnings (£)	No. of operatives
<50	2
50 and <60	60
60 and <70	123
70 and <80	260
80 and <90	197
90 and <100	165
100 and <110	118
110 and <120	51
120 and over	14

Using the above data, calculate the arithmetic mean and standard deviation of weekly earnings of the factory operatives.

Are there any advantages in using the median and quartiles to analyse this distribution?

(Institute of Commercial Management 1985)

The monthly sales achieved by the salesmen of a company for its products A and B are given as follows:

| | Number of salesmen | |
Value of sales (£000)	A	B
<2	5	8
2 and <4	18	22
4 and <6	27	33
6 and <8	31	25
8 and <10	16	10
10 and <15	3	2

(i) Find the mean and the standard deviation of the value of the sales for both products A and B. (10 marks)

(ii) Draw the histograms for product A and product B on the same graph. (6 marks)

(iii) Comment on what your answers to parts (i) and (ii) show. (4 marks)

(Association of Business Executives 1987)

4 | Probability

■ 4.1 INTRODUCTION

Probability and chance are two words frequently used to describe situations about which we are uncertain. They are used in much the same way and mean much the same thing. We may talk about the chance of it raining and whether or not we need to take an umbrella, or the probability of our winning the football pools. We do not know whether or not it will rain, nor do we know if we will win the football pools, but if forced to make some estimate of how likely these events are, we may well say that it is quite probable that it will rain, but very unlikely that we will win the pools.

The idea of probability is well established, and even the idea that it is subject to some sort of assessment. We talk about a good chance of something happening, or a poor chance of something else, usually basing our assessment on experience.

Most business situations involve some element of uncertainty, and many business decisions are based upon an estimate of probability, but vague qualitative estimates like good and poor are not very precise, and experience is often a poor guide.

In this chapter we will be defining the idea of probability rather more precisely than is done in normal conversation, and establishing precise, quantitative measures which will permit much more rigorous and rational use of the concept. We will also identify certain mathematical laws which probability follows (the 'laws of chance' really do exist).

In section 4.2 we will be looking at a precise definition of probability, and its measurement. In section 4.3 we will look at the first law of chance, the **addition rule**, while in 4.4 we will look at the second law of chance, the **multiplication rule**. In section 4.5 we will look at some alternative ways of representing probability issues.

■ 4.2 WHAT IS PROBABILITY?

If you toss a coin it will either land with the 'head' facing upwards or the 'tail' facing upwards (for the purposes of this example, and all other illustrations using coins, we will ignore such outcomes as the coin landing on edge or disappearing through a crack in the floor). Assuming that both the coin and the toss are fair, we would agree that there is an equal chance of a head or a tail (this is actually the definition of a fair coin), and that one of these outcomes must happen. We might speak of the chance of a head being 50 per cent, but if we were using rigorous terminology we would say that the probability of a head is 0.5.

Certain rules govern the way probability is represented mathematically. Key among them are the following:

> Certainty is represented by a probability of 1.0, so something which is bound to happen is said to have a probability of 1.0 and no higher probability can exist (nothing can be more than certain to happen).
> Impossibility is represented by a probability of 0.0, so something which cannot happen is said to have a probability of zero and no lower probability can exist.

We thus have a situation where all probabilities must lie between 0.0 and 1.0. A common way of representing probabilities is as follows:

$$P(H) = 0.5$$

which would, in the case of our coin tossing example, mean:

> the probability of a head is equal to 0.5

On occasion, it is the probability of something not happening which is of interest. If we wish to represent the probability of a head *not* occurring we would say:

$$P(\bar{H})$$

The bar over the top of a symbol in probability equations means not.

This is how probability is represented, but how is it measured? How do we know that the probability of a head is 0.5? How do we find out what the probability of it raining is?

The only satisfactory answer to the question 'What is probability?' is that it is the long-run average rate of occurrence. To find the probability of a head occurring when you toss a coin, you must toss the coin a large number of times, count the number of times it falls heads, and divide this by the total. If we were to toss a coin 1 000 times and got 486 heads we would have to conclude that the probability of a head was 486/1000 or:

$$P(H) = 0.486$$

This is not 0.5, and this represents the difference between theoretical probability and empirical probability.

To toss a coin enough times, without introducing any bias into the way in which we toss it, to be sure of getting exactly 50 per cent heads and 50 per cent tails, is both difficult and time-consuming, so wherever possible we try to create a theoretical model which enables us to deduce probabilities. In the case of the coin, we say that only two outcomes are possible (heads or tails) and that there is no reason to suppose that one outcome is more likely than another. Since something is bound to happen (probability of 1.0) the probability of any one outcome is the total probability divided by the number of (equally probable) outcomes, in this case 1.0/2 or 0.5.

Exercise 16
What is the probability of throwing a six with a fair die?

Theoretical probabilities are extremely useful, they save a lot of investigative effort and, provided they are soundly based, are actually more accurate than empirical probabilities. Unfortunately they are only applicable when we have all the facts, and this rarely applies in the real world, even in apparently simple situations. We have seen that the probability of a head when tossing a coin is 0.5, but what is the probability of a drawing pin landing point down when tossed? A thorough study of the mechanics and aerodynamics involved might lead us to a theoretical answer, but it is easier, and more certain to give a usable result, to carry out an experiment and measure the empirical probability. In most real-life situations, probability is something which is measured. We measure it by recording the number of times the particular outcome, or outcomes, of interest occur, and divide that by the total number of observations. In an ongoing situation, we would continue measuring and improving our estimate of probability by increasing the number of observations.

Exercise 17
You have tossed a drawing pin and obtained the following results:

Landed point down	*897*
Landed point up	*1342*

What is the probability of a drawing pin landing point down when tossed?

■ 4.3 THE ADDITION RULE

When considering probability we are frequently interested in more than one outcome. In manufacturing, for instance, we might have a process which produces defectives which must be scrapped, and defectives which can be reworked to make them usable. It is quite possible that there might be two or more different types of defect that can be reworked in different ways. We would, of course, need to know the probability of a defect of each different type arising so that we could allow enough process capacity for the various rework processes, and so that we could calculate their costs, but we would also want to know the total probability of rework of any sort being required, and the total probability of any sort of defect arising. This is also necessary for capacity planning and costing.

The addition rule says that when you are interested in the total probability of two or more alternative outcomes, you simply add their individual probabilities. Mathematically:

$$P(A \text{ or } B \text{ or } C \text{ etc.}) = P(A) + P(B) + P(C) \text{ etc.}$$

We anticipated this rule in section 4.2 when we defined theoretical probability as 1.0/(the number of equally probable outcomes), so that, in the case of our coin:

$$P(H) + P(T) = 1.0$$

Considering our various classes of defectives, let us consider the following observations:

Number manufactured   2400
Number scrapped   378
Number for rework   540

From this we can say that the probabilities are:

P (scrap) $= 378/2400 = 0.1575$
P (rework) $= 540/2400 = 0.225$

If, instead, we had only wished to know the probability of a defective, we would have gathered the following data:

Number manufactured   2400
Number defective   918 (378 + 540)
P (defective) $= 918/2400 = 0.3825$

We have, in effect, added the original numbers of different classes of defectives together. This is exactly the same as adding the probabilities:

$$P \text{ (scrap or rework)} = P \text{ (scrap)} + P \text{ (rework)}$$
$$= 0.1575 + 0.225 = 0.3825$$

Exercise 18
Given a standard pack of playing cards containing fifty-two cards, what is the probability of drawing:

(a) A heart or a diamond
(b) An honour card (a jack, queen, king or ace)?

A useful outcome of the addition rule is that:

$$P(O) + P(\bar{O}) = 1.0$$

where O is the outcome of interest.

The addition rule only applies when the outcomes are **mutually exclusive**. If two outcomes can arise simultaneously, it does not work. For instance, what is the probability of drawing a club or an ace from a pack of playing cards?

The probability of drawing a club is $13/52 = 0.25$ as there are thirteen clubs in the pack of fifty-two cards.

The probability of drawing an ace is $4/52 = 0.0769$ since there are four aces.

By the addition rule:

$$P(C \text{ or } A) = P(C) + P(A) = 0.25 + 0.0769 = 0.3269$$

However, clubs and aces are not mutually exclusive since there is an ace of clubs. If we count up the possible outcomes we find that there are four aces and twelve other clubs, and the true result is:

$P(C \text{ or } A) = (4 + 12)/52 = 16/52 = 0.3077$

Before applying the addition rule, always check that the outcomes are mutually exclusive.

◼ 4.4 THE MULTIPLICATION RULE

The addition rule applies when we are interested in alternatives. The multiplication rule applies when we are interested in multiple, or simultaneous, occurrences.

Returning to our coin in section 4.2, let us add a second coin and toss both. The outcomes we can have are:

Coin 1	Coin 2
H	H
H	T
T	H
T	T

There are four possible outcomes, all equally probable. Two heads occur once, and two tails once, while a head and a tail occur twice (we are not interested in distinguishing between the coins) so:

$P(2H) = 0.25$
$P(2T) = 0.25$

and, by the addition rule:

$P(H \text{ and } T) = 0.5$

The multiplication rule simplifies this calculation. It is:

$P(A \text{ and } B \text{ and } C \text{ etc.}) = P(A) \times P(B) \times P(C) \text{ etc.}$

so that the probability of two heads is:

$P(H \text{ and } H) = P(H) \times P(H) = 0.5 \times 0.5 = 0.25$

and

$P(T \text{ and } T) = P(T) \times P(T) = 0.5 \times 0.5 = 0.25$

and

$P(H \text{ and } T) = P(H) \times P(T) = 0.5 \times 0.5 = 0.25$

This last result is not wrong because we must also consider $P(T \text{ and } H)$.

The multiplication rule is not just concerned with simultaneous outcomes, but also with consecutive, or even totally unconnected, outcomes. A common fallacy is the belief that if a coin has come up heads ten times running, it is very likely to come up tails next. The multiplication rule will tell us the probability of ten consecutive heads. It is 0.5^{10} which is 0.0009765. It will also tell us the probability of eleven consecutive heads. This is 0.5^{11} or 0.0004882. This is very small, about 5 in 10 000 times, but if we have already had ten consecutive heads, they have already happened and therefore have a probability of 1.0. The probability of an eleventh head is therefore

$$1.0 \times 0.5 = 0.5$$

We may well suspect the fairness of the coin, but if the coin is fair, then the probability of the 11th or even 111th head is exactly the same as the probability of the first.

Exercise 19
Given a standard pack of playing cards, what is the probability of being dealt a hand of four cards containing:

(a) Four aces
(b) The ace of clubs and three diamonds?

The multiplication rule may only be used if the outcomes are independent. For example, the probability of a defective being produced by a manufacturing process may be 0.01, so the probability of ten consecutive defectives should be 0.01^{10} or 0.0000000000001. This is very small but if the first defective was caused by defective materials going into the process, or by a worn or badly set machine, then we might expect further defectives. The outcomes in this case are not independent of each other because they have a common cause.

◼ 4.5   PRESENTING AND CALCULATING PROBABILITY

4.5.1   Mathematical terminology

We have already seen the use of the following:

$P(O)$ the probability of the outcome O
$P(\bar{O})$ the probability of anything other than O
$P(A \text{ and } B)$ the probability of both A and B
$P(A \text{ or } B)$ the probability of either A or B

There are, unfortunately, a number of different sets of mathematical terminology in this field, so you may well find these expressions presented differently in different circumstances.

It often helps to present complex probability situations diagrammatically. Two common methods are as follows.

4.5.2   The Venn diagram

This is a simple sketch map approach to the situation which helps to identify those outcomes which are mutually exclusive and those which are not. Sketching a Venn

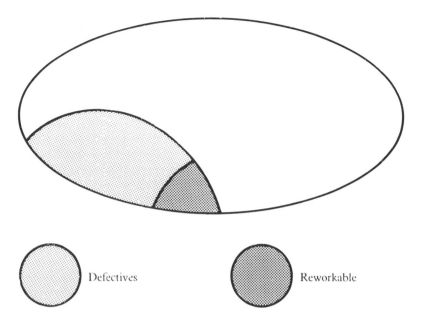

Fig. 25   Venn diagram of defects

diagram helps to identify the various outcome classes which exist, and helps us to decide precisely which are of interest. Considering again the problem of production of defectives that we looked at in section 4.3, a Venn diagram would look like that in Fig. 25. The total area represents all production; within this we have an area representing all rejects, which in its turn contains a smaller area representing reworkable rejects.

Exercise 20
Draw a Venn diagram to illustrate the probability of drawing a club or an ace from a pack of playing cards.

Venn diagrams are approximate scale maps of the situation. Having identified all the categories and sub-categories, we can clearly identify the ones of interest and verify their mutual exclusivity.

4.5.3   The probability tree

The probability tree is a way of showing all possible outcomes. It can be tedious to draw, but it does guarantee that everything is considered. It is used where we are dealing with multiple events, whether simultaneous or consecutive. In other words, where the multiplication rule would be used.

We start with the first event and draw every possible outcome as a branch. At the end of each branch we draw the second event, with each possible outcome as a branch, and so on. Sequence is not usually important (i.e. it does not matter whether we look at coin one or coin two first). Figure 26 shows the probability tree for the tossing of three coins.

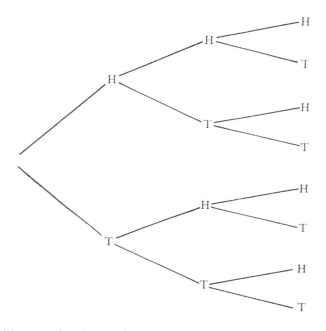

Fig. 26   Probability tree for three coins

The probability of any one outcome can be found from a probability tree by counting the number of end branches and dividing this into 1.0. This gives the probability of any one branch. We then count how many times the same outcome arises and multiply this by the probability of any one branch. In the case of the three coins, there are eight outcomes, so the probability of any one is 1/8. Three heads (and three tails) occur only once, so their probability is precisely 1/8, while two heads and a tail (and two tails and a head) occur three times each, so their probability is 3/8.

We can mix actions with different numbers of outcomes in a probability tree provided each outcome for any one action is equally probable. Exercise 21 illustrates this.

Exercise 21
Draw a probability tree to show outcomes of tossing a fair coin once and of throwing a fair die once. What is the probability of a head and a six?

4.5.4   Permutations and combinations

Once we get involved in multiple events, we have to start considering the number of ways in which things can happen. For instance, when looking at the probabilities involved in tossing three coins, we can readily see that the only possible outcomes are:

Three heads (3H); two heads and a tail (2HT); one head and two tails (H2T); three tails (3T)

The only question we need to ask in order to obtain the probabilities is 'How many ways can two heads and one tail (or two tails and one head) be arranged?' Of course, the probability tree tells us that the answer is three, but consider drawing a probability tree for ten coins.

Let us arrange six different coloured beads in a row. We can obviously arrange them in a number of different sequences. We have six choices for first position, but having put a bead in the first position, we now have only five left, giving us five choices for the second position, four for the third and so on. This is very similar to the sort of probability tree you might get if you consider the throwing of six dice, except that there is one less outcome at each successive event.

We could draw a tree and count the ends, but a much simpler way is available. We simply multiply the consecutive numbers of choices thus:

Number of arrangements = $6 \times 5 \times 4 \times 3 \times 2 \times 1 = 720$

This is obviously much better than drawing a tree with 720 terminal branches.

In mathematical terminology, the number of ways of arranging N different things is:

$N!$ (called N factorial)

where ! means multiply together every number between 1 and N.

If we select three beads at random from our six, then there are still six ways of selecting the first, five of the second, and four of the third. Since that is all we are allowed, then there are obviously $6 \times 5 \times 4 = 120$ ways of arranging three from six. There is no mathematical symbol for this, but it is called a **permutation** and its general formula is:

$$^{n}P_{r} = \frac{n!}{(n - r)!}$$

where n is the total number and r is the number chosen.

Note that it is necessary for 0! to be equal to 1 for this and all other uses of factorials to work. There is a theoretical basis for this, but it need not concern us.

In the case of our six beads:

$^{6}P_{3} = 6!/(6 - 3)! = 6!/3! = 720/6 = 120$

Exercise 22
How many arrangements of five beads chosen at random from eight different beads are there?

We are, in practice, rarely interested in order. We are much more likely to want to know how many different sets of beads can be obtained than how many different sequences. In the case of tossing three coins, we are not interested in the sequence of heads and tails, only in the number.

Having picked three beads we know that there are $3! = 6$ ways of ordering them. The 120 different permutations are ways of choosing $\times$ ways of ordering the resultant choice. If we are not interested in the order, then we divide the permutation by the number of different orders to get the number of sets independent of order. There are $120/6 = 20$ ways of choosing three beads from six.

This is called a **combination** and is expressed mathematically as:

$$^nC_r = \frac{n!}{r!(n-r)!}$$

The football pools is a well-known example of combinations. One is required to pick eight correct matches from a list of fifty or so in order to win the maximum prize (we will not for the moment worry about the criteria for correctness, or the fact that there may be more than eight matches which satisfy these criteria). The order in which the matches are selected is of no importance, so the basic problem is selecting the correct combination from:

$$^{50}C_8 = 50!/(8!(50-8)!) = 50!/(8!42!)$$

You may well find that this is beyond the capacity of your calculator, but it comes to 536 878 650. Assuming that each combination is equally likely to be the winning one, then the probability of any one combination of eight matches winning is 1/536 878 650, which is as near zero as makes no difference as far as the author is concerned.

Exercise 23
Calculate:

(a) $^6C_4$
(b) $^7C_3$

In the coin-tossing examples we were actually looking at combinations. If we toss a coin four times, we know that there are $2 \times 2 \times 2 \times 2$ $(2^4) = 16$ equally probable outcomes. We know that these will be 4H, 3HT, 2H2T, H3T and 4T. The only other piece of information we need is in how many ways, ignoring order, can we obtain 3H from 4, 2H from 4 and 1H from 4. These are, of course, $^4C_3$, $^4C_2$ and $^4C_1$, which are:

$$^4C_3 = 4$$
$$^4C_2 = 6$$
$$^4C_1 = 4$$

The multiplication rule tells us that the probability of 2H2T occurring in any one way is:

$$P(H) \times P(H) \times P(T) \times P(T) = 0.5^4 = 0.0625$$

Since we know from combinations that it can occur in six different ways, the addition rule tells us that the probability of 2H2T is:

$$^4C_2 \times 0.0625 = 6 \times 0.0625 = 0.375$$

Exercise 24
What is the probability of:

(a) *Getting only one head when throwing four coins*
(b) *Getting four or more heads when throwing five coins?*

■ 4.6   SUMMARY

In this chapter we have looked at the concept of probability and defined it as the long-run average rate of occurrence of the outcome of interest. We have seen that in some situations we can derive probability from theoretical considerations, but that in most real-life situations we need to measure it by collecting data. We have shown that probability is subject to certain mathematical rules, and we have looked at the mathematical functions of factorial, permutation and combination as ways of simplifying the calculation of probabilities, and at the Venn diagram and probability tree as ways of simplifying their presentation.

As it stands, our knowledge of probability does not seem to be much use unless we are committed gamblers. In the next chapter we will see that probabilistic behaviour often follows well-defined patterns, and it is the use of these patterns which makes statistical methods in general and probability in particular such a powerful tool.

■ 4.7   STUDY AND EXAM TIPS

A question only about probability is unlikely, but probability may well be an important element of questions of a more general nature.

1 Make sure that you understand what the question is asking. It is very easy to get confused with questions asking for the probability of x or y. Does it mean either x or y or both, or x or y but not both? Does a question asking for the probability of ten defectives in a batch of fifty mean ten and only ten, or at least ten? Draw a Venn diagram: this often shows the situation more clearly than words can. If there still seems to be ambiguity, state your assumptions about the question clearly (e.g. 'I assume that this question requires the probability of either x or y, but not both x and y, for the following reasons ...).

Examiners go to a lot of trouble to ensure that questions are not ambiguous, so do be sure that you are not simply misunderstanding the question.

2 Do not just key everything into your calculator and simply write down the final answer. It may be wrong, and if the examiner cannot follow your method you will get no credit. Write down the formulae and the intermediate steps, then, if your answer is wrong, you will get credit for method (assuming it is correct).

3 It is always a good idea to do a rough check on calculations, to see that your answer is at least of the correct order of magnitude. It is all too easy to go wrong when keying in things like 8! or 0.2^9.

■ SELF ASSESSMENT QUESTIONS

Answer the following questions and then check your answers against those at the end of the book. If you get any wrong, re-read the relevant parts of the chapter. If this does not help, then talk to your tutor about the problem.

1 The probability of a head occurring only once in tossing two coins is:
(a) 0.5
(b) 0.125
(c) 0.75
(d) 1.0

2 6! is:
(a) 24
(b) 540
(c) 720
(d) 1500

3 The probability of throwing a six followed by a five with a fair die is:
(a) 1/6
(b) 0.5
(c) 1/3
(d) 1/36
(e) 1/24

4 The probability of throwing a six or a five with a fair die is:
(a) 1/6
(b) 0.5
(c) 1/3
(d) 1/36
(e) 1/24

■ EXAMINATION QUESTIONS

A petrol company proposes to open a new petrol filling station. From a survey of the site and a knowledge of their other stations they estimate that if they install six petrol pumps, the probability that at any instant any one of the pumps is engaged by a car requiring petrol is 0.3.

   (a) Calculate the probability that all six pumps will be engaged. (3 marks)

   (b) Calculate the probability that exactly one pump will be engaged. (4 marks)

   (c) Calculate the probability that at least two of the pumps will be engaged. (5 marks)

(Institute of Marketing 1987)

Your company is seeking to tender for the selling franchise in three overseas markets, A, B and C. It estimates that the probability that it will secure tender A is 0.2, tender B is 0.3 and tender C is 0.4. Find the probability that your company will:
  (i) Obtain all three franchises. (4 marks)
  (ii) Obtain only one franchise. (6 marks)

(*Institute of Marketing 1988*)

Note: pure probability questions are rare, and neither of these examples is a full question.

5 Distributions

■ 5.1 INTRODUCTION

We have seen in Chapter 4 how we can calculate the probability of any outcome, or set of outcomes, from the basic definition of probability, and from the two 'laws of chance'. This can be done on theoretical grounds, as with dice and coins, or empirically, as with most problems of real interest.

As we gather more and more data about different situations we begin to find the same patterns of behaviour occurring again and again, and we find that situations can be classified according to the pattern of the probabilities of the various outcomes. For example, when we toss a coin there are precisely two outcomes (head or tail) and they each have a probability of 0.5. If we toss a drawing pin there are again precisely two outcomes (pin up or pin down). If we take a sample from a production process and test it, we can arrange to have precisely two outcomes (good or reject). While the probabilities may no longer be 0.5, we would calculate the probability of two rejects or 200 rejects in exactly the same way as we would calculate the probability of two heads or 200 heads. The distribution of probabilities in these three situations follow the same rules.

There are a number of different **probability distributions**, and with a little practice and experience you will begin to recognise which is likely to apply in which situation.

Knowing the probability distribution that applies greatly simplifies the analysis of any situation involving probability, and our knowledge of the behaviour of the probability distribution in question can often allow us to extract far more information from the data than would otherwise be possible. In other words, probability distributions actually offer us more information for less effort.

In this chapter we will look at the three most common distributions (we will look at three others in Chapter 9).

In section 5.2 we will look at the **binomial** distribution, in 5.3 the **Poisson** distribution and in 5.4 the **normal** distribution. In section 5.5 we will consider the circumstances in which they might be used interchangeably.

■ 5.2 THE BINOMIAL DISTRIBUTION

The binomial distribution is applicable in situations where we are concerned with only two possible outcomes. The example we used in Chapter 4 of tossing a coin is typical. Usually we are dealing with an event (the toss of the coin) which is certain to take place (i.e. has a probability of 1.0) and which leads to an outcome which will fall into one of two mutually exclusive classes (i.e. head or tail). Examples from industry and commerce include:

Is that component defective or not?
Will we win that contract or not?
Is a worker absent or not?

Binomial situations usually rely on counting and classification, but not on measurement, so we would not use the binomial distribution for something like the weight of a bag of sugar or people's height. However, any measurement can be divided into two classes, so we could apply the binomial distribution if we classed bags of sugar as being either <1 kilogram or $\geqslant 1$ kilogram (or people being <160 cm tall or $\geqslant 160$ cm tall). In quality control in particular, we are often concerned with measuring particular attributes of the product (weight, thickness, strength etc.), but in the last analysis we are really only concerned with whether or not the product is acceptable.

Expressed mathematically, the binomial situation reduces to:

$$p + q = 1$$

where p is the probability of the outcome of interest occurring and q is the probability of any other outcomes occurring. If we consider coin tossing, then:

$$0.5 + 0.5 = 1.0$$

or a machine producing 10 per cent defectives:

$$0.1 + 0.9 = 1.0$$

This, of course, represents only one event, one toss of the coin or one component produced. We are usually interested in more than one event and the binomial distribution for n events is represented by:

$$(p + q)^n = 1.0$$

If we expand this equation we find that the individual terms represent the probabilities of each alternative set of outcomes, for example:

$$(p + q)^3 = p^3 + 3p^2q + 3pq^2 + q^3$$

where p^3 is the probability of the outcome of interest arising three times out of three, $3p^2q$ the probability of it arising two times in three and so on.

Of course we already know, from Chapter 4, how to calculate such a probability. The multiplication rule gives us the probability of the outcome happening in any one way (say p^2q). We then multiply that by the number of ways (combinations) in which it can happen. So the probability of the outcome of interest occurring two times out of three is:

$$^3C_2p^2q \text{ and } ^3C_2 = 3$$

The general term for the probability of the outcome of interest arising r times in n events is:

$$P(r \text{ in } n) = {}^nC_rp^rq^{(n-r)}$$

To illustrate the use of this, let us consider a process producing a component in batches of ten, with the probability of a defective being 0.1. We have:

$$p = 0.1$$
$$q = 1.0 - p = 0.9$$
$$n = 10$$

What is the probability of any one batch containing precisely three defectives? We now have:

$$r = 3$$

and all the information we need to work out the probability, which is:

$$P(3 \text{ in } 10) = {}^{10}C_3 \times 0.1^3 \times 0.9^{(10-3)}$$

$$= \frac{3\,628\,800 \times 0.001 \times 0.4783}{5040 \times 6}$$

$$= 0.0574$$

We may, of course, be interested in the probability of say seven or more rejects in a batch. In order to keep the numbers manageable, the following example assumes a probability of a reject of 0.2. We know from the addition rule that:

$$P(7 \text{ or } 8 \text{ or } 9 \text{ or } 10) = P(7) + P(8) + P(9) + P(10)$$

and:

$$P(7) = {}^{10}C_7 \times 0.2^7 \times 0.8^3 = 120 \times 0.0000128 \times 0.512$$
$$= 0.0007864$$
$$P(8) = {}^{10}C_8 \times 0.2^8 \times 0.8^2 = 45 \times 0.00000256 \times 0.64$$
$$= 0.00007373$$
$$P(9) = {}^{10}C_9 \times 0.2^9 \times 0.8 = 10 \times 0.000000512 \times 0.8$$
$$= 0.000004096$$
$$P(10) = 0.2^{10} = 0.000000102$$

so:

$$P(\geqslant 7) = 0.0007864 + 0.00007373 + 0.000004096 + 0.000000102$$
$$= 0.00086433$$

Exercise 25
A process produces batches of ten with a probability of a reject of 0.05. What is the probability of more than two rejects in a batch?
(Hint: $P(>2 \text{ in } 10) = 1.0 - P(\leqslant 2 \text{ in } 10)$)

For small numbers of events, **Pascal's pyramid** can be a short cut to finding the number of ways in which the outcome can arise. It is illustrated in Table 23.

The numbers represent the number of combinations appropriate to the successive terms in the expansion of $(p + q)^n$. For example, if we are concerned with $(p + q)^4$, we would multiply the terms p^4, p^3q, p^2q^2 etc. by the numbers in the row corresponding to $n = 4$ to obtain the probabilities thus:

$$1p^4 + 4p^3q + 6p^2q^2 + 4pq^3 + 1q^4$$

Table 23 Pascal's pyramid

n															
1							1		1						
2						1		2		1					
3					1		3		3		1				
4				1		4		6		4		1			
5			1		5		10		10		5		1		
6		1		6		15		20		15		6		1	
7	1		7		21		35		35		21		7		1

Each row of the pyramid begins and ends with 1, and the internal values are found by adding together the two adjacent values on the row above. This approach is only worthwhile if you can sketch a pyramid of the requisite size more quickly than you can calculate the necessary combinations.

5.2.1 Mean and standard deviation

One advantage of being able to classify some occurrence as belonging to a specified probability distribution is that we can define the mean and standard deviation precisely. The mean of a binomial distribution is always:

$$np$$

and the standard deviation is:

$$\sqrt{npq}$$

In our original example of batches of ten with a probability of reject of 0.1, the mean is $10 \times 0.1 = 1.0$. This means that over a number of batches we would expect to see an average of one reject per batch. The standard deviation is $\sqrt{10 \times 0.1 \times 0.9} = 0.95$.

Exercise 26
A process produces batches of ten with a probability of a reject of 0.05. What is the mean and the standard deviation?

5.2.2 The shape of the binomial distribution

The shape of the binomial distribution varies with both p and n. Figure 27 shows the variation of shape with p.

As you can see, when p is small the distribution is heavily skewed towards the left. This is, of course, what we would expect: a low probability of an outcome suggests that the outcome would not occur very frequently. As the probability increases, the distribution becomes more and more symmetrical until, at $p = 0.5$, it is perfectly symmetrical. We do not usually consider values of $p > 0.5$; p is always considered the smaller of the two probabilities, and q the larger.

We get a very similar effect as we increase n, as shown in Fig. 28.

Again we would expect this since the larger the number of observations, the

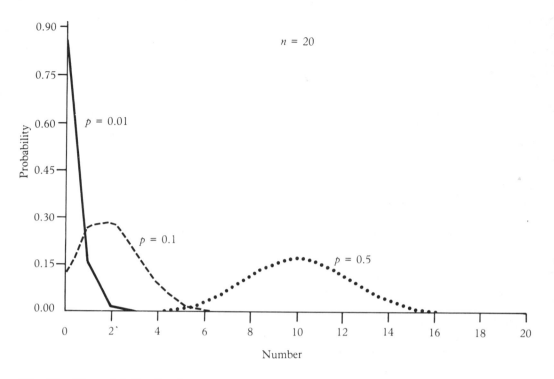

Fig. 27 Binomial distribution

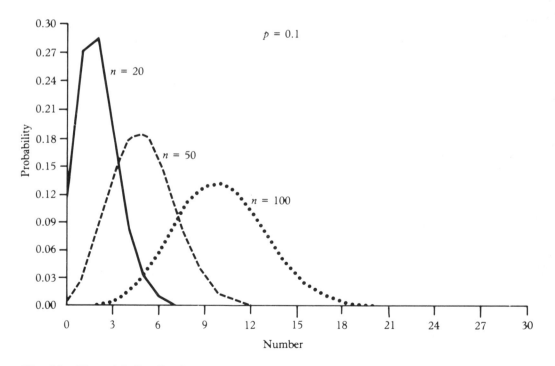

Fig. 28 Binomial distribution

larger the number of occurrences of the outcome of interest, no matter how small its probability.

Both of these trends have important implications for simplifying the use of the binomial distribution when we are dealing with large numbers, as we shall see in section 5.5.

■ 5.3   THE POISSON DISTRIBUTION

There are occasions when we are interested not in the outcome of an event, but in whether or not the event takes place at all. It makes sense to talk about how frequently we have a satisfactory meal in a restaurant, as compared with how frequently we have an unsatisfactory meal, and this is a binomial situation since the meal is the event and we are concerned with the outcome. We can equally talk about how often we find a five-pound note in the street, but we cannot talk about how often we do not find a five-pound note, because we cannot define the event for which not finding a five-pound note is an outcome.

What we are considering here are events taking place at random. Such events frequently fall into the category of 'accidents', and are therefore of great interest to insurance companies, among others. They are characterised by the need to specify a time limit when talking about probabilities. To talk sensibly about the probability of a house being struck by lightning, we must specify whether we mean this week, this year, or during the next ten years.

Wherever the outcome and the event itself are indistinguishable, for example, all accidents, the arrival of customers at a service facility, the arrival of cars at a road junction, the breakdown of machines, we use the Poisson probability distribution.

There is, unfortunately, no simple explanation of the formula for the Poisson distribution or, indeed, for any distribution other than the binomial, so we must simply take the formula on trust. It is:

$$P(c) = e^{-a}a^c/c!$$

where c is the number of occurrences of interest, a is the mean rate of occurrences, e is the **exponential**, a constant which often crops up in statistics and has a value of 2.71828.... It is often found built into calculators and computer programs.

If we are running a restaurant, we may be interested in the probability of a given number of customers arriving within a given time. This information might be used to decide on how many tables to have, how many staff, how much food to stock etc. All we need to know is the mean rate of arrival of customers (this would, of course, probably vary from hour to hour and from day to day, and we may have to consider separately the mean rate of arrival on, for example, Monday lunchtime and Saturday evening). If the mean rate of arrival is ten per hour, then the probability that four and only four people will arrive in any one hour is given by:

$$P(4) = e^{-10}10^4/4!$$
$$= 0.0000454 \times 10\,000/24$$
$$= 0.0189$$

We may wish to consider a smaller time interval, say 10 minutes. All we need do to achieve this is work out the mean rate of arrival per 10 minutes and substitute this into the formula:

Mean rate per 60 minutes = 10, therefore
Mean rate per 10 minutes = $10 \times 10/60 = 1.67$
$P(4 \text{ in } 10 \text{ minutes}) = e^{-1.67}1.67^4/4!$
$\qquad\qquad\qquad\qquad = 0.1889 \times 7.72/24$
$\qquad\qquad\qquad\qquad = 0.0608$

It may surprise you that this is a higher probability than we obtained when considering one hour, but we are considering *only* four customers, and it is very likely that more than four will arrive in an hour.

Exercise 27
What is the probability of exactly six customers arriving in any half hour?

When considering problems like 'the probability of three or less', then we have no option but to calculate the probability of zero, one, two and three and add them together. Books of statistical tables do have tables of Poisson probabilities but, given the infinite range of possible means, they are of limited value. If the question is something like 'the probability of four or more' we must calculate the probability of three or less and subtract this from one since Poisson probabilities go on to infinity (there is never a number beyond which no further occurrences can arise). Self-evidently, questions like 'the probability of three to seven inclusive' are also answered by finding the individual probabilities and using the addition rule.

Exercise 28
A mail-order company receives an average of one call every two minutes. What is the probability that it will receive more than five calls in five minutes?

5.3.1 The mean and standard deviation of the Poisson distribution

The mean of the Poisson distribution is, of course, a; its standard deviation is $\sqrt{a}$.

5.3.2 The shape of the Poisson distribution

With the Poisson distribution, we only have the variable a to concern us. Figure 29 shows that, as we would expect, the distribution becomes more symmetrical as a increases.

■ 5.4 THE NORMAL DISTRIBUTION

The normal distribution differs from the binomial and Poisson distributions in being concerned with continuous variables rather than discrete events. With the binomial distribution we are concerned with a particular outcome of an event,

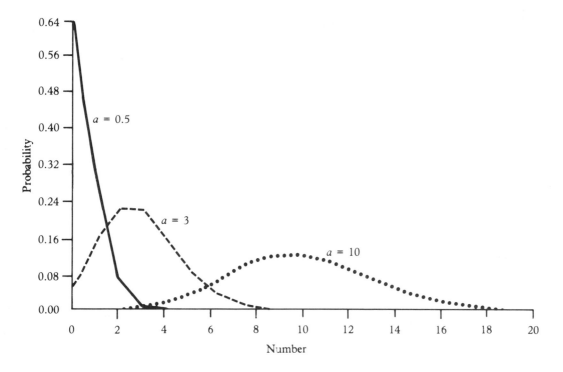

Fig. 29 Poisson distribution

while with the Poisson distribution we are concerned with whether or not an event occurred at all. In both cases we are counting events. As we have seen, almost anything can be classified in this way, but we are frequently interested in looking at actual measurements. The binomial distribution can tell us the probability of finding ten oversize components in a batch of 100, but if we change the size specification, we have to start data collection all over again. If we had collected information on actual size rather than just oversize or not, the normal distribution would allow us to calculate reject probabilities for any specification. Counting is always easier and cheaper than measuring, but it always gives much less information.

Let us imagine that we have a machine for bagging sugar, and it is set to produce bags with a mean weight of 1 kg, with a standard deviation of 0.02 kg. This is the sort of process which typically produces a normal distribution. If we weighed 100 consecutive bags, we might get a distribution like that shown in Fig. 30.

If we were to weigh 200 bags, but were to classify them with an increment of 0.01 kg instead of 0.02 kg, we would get the distribution shown in Fig. 31. You will notice that although we have doubled the number of bags, the *y* axis remains much the same because we have halved the group size. Because the number of bags is greater, and the group size smaller, we also have a better picture of the shape of the distribution.

If we re-label the *x* axis so that the mean is zero and the standard deviation is one, we have what is called a **standardised** distribution. This is shown in Fig. 32.

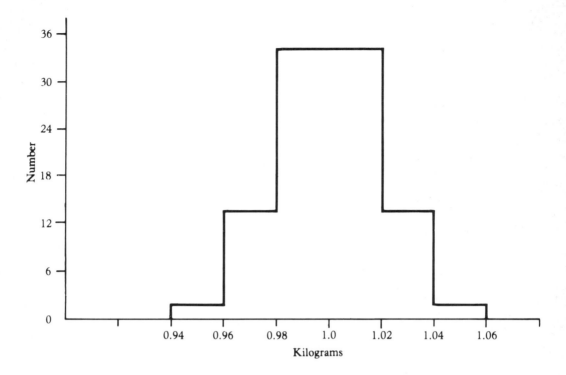

Fig. 30 100 bags of sugar

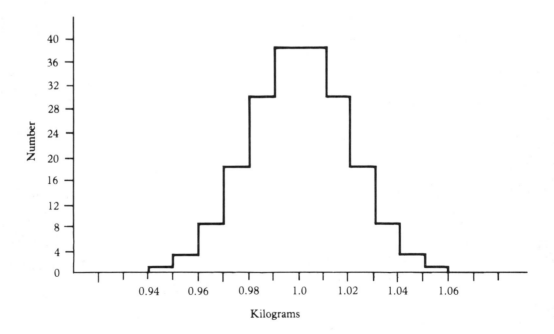

Fig. 31 200 bags of sugar

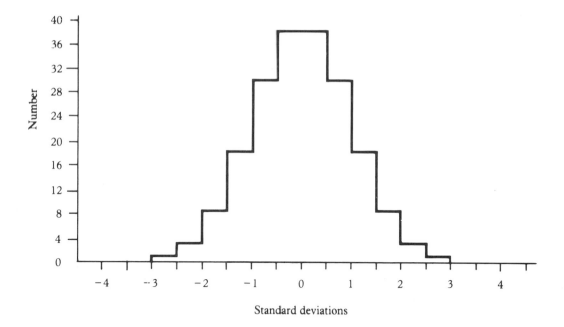

Fig. 32   200 bags of sugar

If we were to continue doubling the number of bags weighed, and halving the group size, the histogram would gradually come to resemble a smooth curve. It would reach that position when we had weighed an infinite number of bags and had an infinitesimally small group size. It would no longer make any sense to label the *y* axis and we would have plotted the **probability density** of the normal distribution. This is shown in Fig. 33.

The total area under the curve represents a probability of 1.0, and the area between any two values on the *x* axis represents the probability of that range of values occurring. We need not concern ourselves with the theoretical basis behind the normal distribution, but we do need to be aware of some of its properties. The most important are:

It is symmetrical about the mean. There is a 0.5 probability of a value being less than the mean, and a 0.5 probability of a value being greater than the mean. A side effect of this is that the mean, median and mode are all equal.
It has no limits. Any value, no matter how large, whether positive or negative, is theoretically possible.
It applies exactly only to continuous variables.

As we have seen, the key statistical measures when dealing with continuous variables are the mean and the standard deviation. If we had to concern ourselves with a probability distribution for every possible combination of mean and standard deviation, we would be in considerable difficulty. Fortunately, the shape of the normal distribution, expressed in terms of the mean and standard deviation, is constant. This is called the **standard normal distribution**.

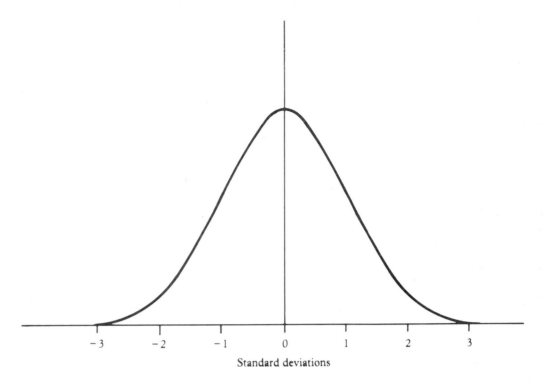

Fig. 33   Standard normal distribution

In order to use the normal distribution we must first obtain the mean and standard deviation for our data. Next we define the range of interest in terms of the standard normal distribution and, finally, we look up the probability in a table. A table of the normal distribution is shown in Appendix 3.

Let us look at a few examples of its use:

If we are packing 1 kg bags of sugar we may be concerned about the probability of underweight bags arising. Since the normal distribution is theoretically infinite, we can never say that underweight bags are impossible. We already know that the standard deviation is 0.02 kg. What is the probability of a bag being less than 1 kg if we set our machine to a mean of 1.03 kg?

It is always a good idea to sketch the problem and then there can be no confusion about which area of the curve we are looking at. Figure 34 shows the problem.

We need to find out how many standard deviations away from the mean our minimum of 1 kg is. This statistic, number of standard deviations away from the mean, is usually referred to as z.

$$z = \frac{(\text{Mean} - \text{limit})}{\text{Standard deviation}}$$

or $z = (1.03 - 1.00)/0.02 = 1.5$

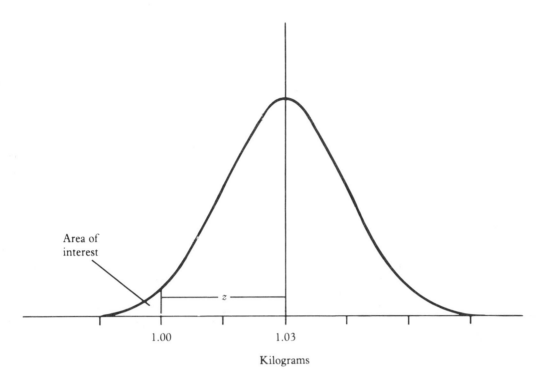

Fig. 34   Probability of <1 kg

The table only gives one half of the distribution (it is symmetrical and the other half would be identical), but what we are interested in here is the area furthest from the mean, and if we find 1.5 in the column labelled z, we find a probability of 0.0668. If we set the machine at 1.035 kg we get

$$z = (1.035 - 1.000)/0.02 = 1.75$$

Looking up 1.75 in the column headed z, we find a probability of 0.0406.

Exercise 29
What is the probability of an underweight bag if the machine is set at 1.045 kg?

An alternative approach to this problem is to say that we will accept only a 1 per cent probability of underweight bags, and use the table to find the required value of z. We look for 0.01 (1 per cent) in the body of the table, and find that the nearest figures are 0.0107 at $z = 2.30$ and 0.0094 at $z = 2.35$. If we need absolute accuracy at this stage, then we need a set of tables which goes to more decimal places. In this case we certainly don't need absolute accuracy, so we can either say z is about 2.325, or err on the side of caution and use $z = 2.35$. If we adopt the latter approach, then our new setting should be:

$$1.00 + 0.02 \times 2.35 = 1.047 \text{ kg}$$

Exercise 30
What machine setting do we need for a probability of being underweight of 2.5%?

We are often interested in both ends of the range, for instance we may be trying to machine metal rods to a tolerance of ± 0.05 mm, with a mean of 5 mm. In this case anything less than 4.95 mm or greater than 5.05 mm will be out of specification. If our process has a standard deviation of 0.015 mm, what is the probability of a reject if the process is set to produce with a mean of 5.00 mm?

We need to calculate z for both the upper and lower limit, find the probability in both cases and add them together.

Upper: $z = (5.05 - 5.00)/0.015 = 3.33$

From the table, $p = 0.00048$ at 3.3 and 0.00034 at 3.4. We find an approximate result by interpolation: 3.33 is 30 per cent of the way between 3.3 and 3.4, so p is $0.00048 - 0.3 \times (0.00048 - 0.00034) = 0.00044$.

Lower: $z = (5.00 - 4.95)/0.015 = 3.33$
and again $p = 0.00044$

So the total probability of a reject $= 0.00088$.

Exercise 31
What is the probability of a reject if the process is set to give a mean of 5.01 mm?

Occasionally we are interested in intermediate areas of the distribution, for instance if the mean height of adults is 173 cm, with a standard deviation of 8 cm, what is the probability of someone being between 175 and 185 cm tall?

We need to calculate z for both limits:

$$z_1 = (175 - 173)/8 = 0.25$$
and $$z_2 = (185 - 173)/8 = 1.5$$

From the table:

$$p_1 = 0.4013$$
and $$p_2 = 0.0668$$

Figure 35 shows a sketch of the problem, and from this it is clear that the answer is the difference between those two probabilities or 0.3345.

Exercise 32
What is the probability of someone being between 165 and 180 cm tall?

A useful rule of thumb on the normal distribution is that 95 per cent of values lie within ± 2 (strictly 1.96) standard deviations, and 99.7 per cent within ± 3 standard deviations.

■ 5.5 WHICH DISTRIBUTION?

The circumstances in which we would use the three distributions should, by now, be obvious. We use the binomial distribution when there are precisely two outcomes (or when the data has been classified in such a way that there are precisely two outcomes), the Poisson when we are considering random events, and the normal when we are dealing with continuous variables.

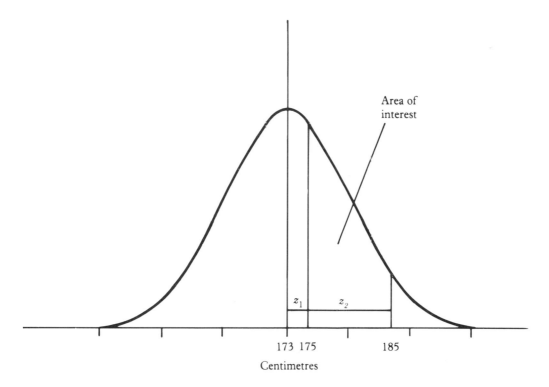

Fig. 35 Probability of 175–185 cm tall

It should be noted that continuous variables do not always follow the normal distribution, and we should at least check that the distribution is more or less symmetrical, and that the range is around four to six standard deviations. In the electronics industry, components are often sold to different tolerances (e.g. ± 5 or ± 10 per cent) with the narrower tolerance commanding a higher price. Since we are dealing with a continuous variable, we would expect the normal distribution to apply, but if an unscrupulous supplier were to separate the ± 5 per cent components out from the rest and sell them separately, neither specification would show a normal distribution. It should be stressed that this is not done.

The advantage of using a distribution to calculate probabilities, rather than using empirical probabilities, is that we obtain a more accurate value because we are using our knowledge of the precise shape of the distribution in addition to the actual statistics that we have available. The disadvantage, particularly in the case of the binomial and Poisson distributions, is the considerable amount of calculation involved. There are situations, and fortunately those involving the greatest amount of calculation, where we can use distributions other than the obvious one.

5.5.1 Poisson for binomial

While not especially easy to use, the Poisson distribution is easier than the binomial. The two distributions are very similar when the binomial situation looks like random events. In other words, when p is small and n is large. Generally the Poisson is considered appropriate if p is less than 0.1 and np, the mean, is greater than about 8. These are general guidelines, the distributions become closer as n increases and p reduces.

5.5.2 Normal for binomial and Poisson

We have seen that both the binomial and Poisson distributions become symmetrical as the mean increases. As they become symmetrical they more and more come to resemble the normal distribution. Again these limits are approximate, but it is generally accepted that the normal distribution can be used for the binomial when p is about 0.5 and np is greater than 8. The normal can be used for Poisson when a is greater than 25.

Remember when using the normal distribution in either situation that it is a continuous distribution. This means that if we were considering, for example, the probability of 20 heads in 100 coin tosses, we must look at the probability of between 19.5 and 20.5 heads.

◼ 5.6 SUMMARY

In this chapter we have seen that there are three well-defined classes of data which generally follow clear rules. These are:

> Events with two outcomes, which follow the binomial distribution
> Random events, which follow the Poisson distribution
> Continuous variables, which follow the normal distribution

We have seen the way in which binomial probabilities can be derived from the addition and multiplication rules, and combinations; how Poisson probabilities can be calculated from a simple formula; and how normal probabilities are simply looked up in a table. We have also considered the situations in which calculation can be simplified by using the Poisson distribution in place of the binomial, and the normal distribution in place of both the binomial and Poisson distributions.

We have identified these distributions as means of gaining greater accuracy for estimates of probability than empirical calculations based on raw data can give. We have not yet considered where that raw data comes from and how reliable it might be. We will look at this in Chapter 7 when we consider sampling.

◼ 5.7 STUDY AND EXAM TIPS

1 The fundamental issue in any question concerned with distributions is the correct identification of the distribution concerned. You must ask yourself:

Am I concerned with continuous variables or with events?
If with events, is it the event itself or the outcome of the event?

This will tell you whether it is normal, Poisson or binomial.

The true issue may be disguised. A question could talk about the probability of a bolt being <9.9 mm or >10.1 mm. This looks like a continuous variable (mm), but is in fact about classifications, so we are looking at the event, a bolt being measured, and the outcomes <9.9, >10.1 or between 9.9 and 10.1. We do not know how to handle a probability distribution for more than two classes, so we must reclassify this into reject (<9.9 or >10.1) and acceptable, and treat it as binomial.

2 Having identified the appropriate distribution, if it is binomial consider using the Poisson or normal approximation. If it is Poisson, consider using the normal approximation. This will simplify the calculation and reduce the time needed to complete the question. You will get no credit for taking the longer route if there is a valid short cut, but do state that you are using the normal approximation for the binomial, or whatever.

3 Remember, when using the normal approximation, to treat your variables as continuous. You cannot find the probability of a single value in the normal tables.

4 When using the normal distribution, always sketch the curve and shade the area of interest. It does not have to be accurate or particularly well drawn, it is a sketch to help you be sure you are looking up the right values in the table.

5 If using the binomial distribution with fairly small numbers (i.e. n less than 6 or so) consider using Pascal's pyramid rather than combinations. It is probably quicker to draw the pyramid than calculate combinations.

6 You can never get a probability of greater than 1.0. Look at your answer and ask yourself if it is reasonable. If it is obviously unreasonable and you cannot see where you have gone wrong, at least say you do not think it can be correct. (Be cautious about this, it is just as bad to say that you think an answer is unreasonable when it is correct as to leave an unreasonably wrong answer without comment.)

■ SELF ASSESSMENT QUESTIONS

Answer the following questions and then check your answers against those at the end of the book. If you get any wrong, re-read the relevant parts of the chapter. If this does not help, then talk to your tutor about the problem.

1 Which distribution would you expect to fit the following:
(a) Tossing a coin
(b) Absenteeism
(c) Throwing a fair die
(d) Heights of people
(e) Salaries of people
(f) Throwing 6 on a fair die
(g) Insurance claims

2 The normal distribution can be used for the binomial when:
(a) p is about 0.5
(b) $np > 8$
(c) $np < 8$
(d) p is small
(e) Never

3 Which of the following apply to the normal distribution:
(a) It is asymmetrical
(b) Mean = mode
(c) The range is about twice the standard deviation
(d) It is symmetrical
(e) The standard deviation is about 1/6th of the range?

4 The mean of the binomial distribution is:
(a) a
(b) npq
(c) $\sqrt{npq}$
(d) np

■ EXAMINATION QUESTIONS

Most examination questions concern themselves with the use of distributions in sampling, and will be found at the end of Chapters 8 and 9.

(a) Describe the necessary conditions for the use of the binomial distribution. (6 marks)

(b) A manager finds that, on average, 10 per cent of his staff are absent through sickness on any one day. He chooses a group of three people at random. What is:

(i) The probability that none of them will be absent from sickness? (3 marks)

(ii) The probability that one of them is absent from sickness? (5 marks)

(iii) The percentage of time that at least two will be present? (6 marks)

(Association of Business Executives 1988)

6 Correlation

■ 6.1 INTRODUCTION

Quite often we are interested in the relationship between two variables, for instance we might expect a relationship between advertising expenditure and sales revenue, or between the weather and absenteeism. If we could establish such a relationship we could use it to match our advertising budget to our sales plans, or to plan our manning levels to allow for different rates of absenteeism in summer and winter, either of which could greatly increase our operating efficiency.

Try to identify some other areas where an ability to predict one figure from another would be useful (e.g. if you were an ice-cream manufacturer you might use weather forecast temperatures to predict sales).

Such relationships are known as **correlations** and can be a very important aid to decision-making. In this chapter we are going to look at the following aspects of correlation.

In section 6.2 we will look at the different patterns of correlation that can arise. In section 6.3 we will see how we can calculate the **correlation coefficient** which gives us a numerical measure of how good the correlation is. In section 6.4 we will look at an alternative correlation coefficient which is used when we only have ranked data rather than precise measurements. In section 6.5 we will look at the interpretation of the correlation coefficient and at some of the pitfalls which can trap the unwary when using correlation.

■ 6.2 WHAT IS CORRELATION?

Correlation is best described by looking at a few examples. We might, for instance, suspect that sales revenue is influenced by advertising expenditure, and have collected the figures shown in Table 24.

It is, of course, quite possible that sales are varying with time (there could be an upward or downward trend).

Tables of figures do not give a very clear picture, so the first stage when looking at correlations is usually to plot the points on a graph. Figures 36 and 37 show the graphs of sales revenue against time and advertising expenditure. Graphs like this (i.e. with only the points marked) are usually called scatter graphs or scatter diagrams.

Table 24 Sales and advertising for Company X

Month	Advertising expenditure (£000)	Sales revenue (£000)
1	5	49
2	9	90
3	9	87
4	8	82
5	7	66
6	8	74
7	4	48
8	6	51

The graphs show us that sales revenue appears to rise with increasing advertising, from which we might assume that sales revenue could be controlled by adjusting advertising expenditure. The relationship between sales revenue and time is far less clear and we might assume that sales are independent of time (i.e. there is no rising or falling sales trend).

Obviously many possible patterns of relationship between two variables exist, and Figs. 38–42 illustrate a range of possibilities. Figure 38 represents a perfect positive correlation, where the y variable rises in exact step with the x variable. Such relationships are rarely found in industry and commerce and are usually the

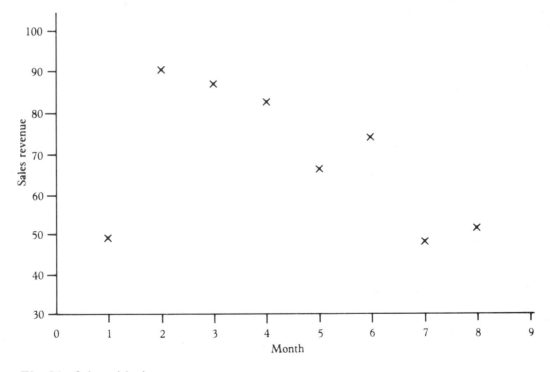

Fig. 36 Sales with time

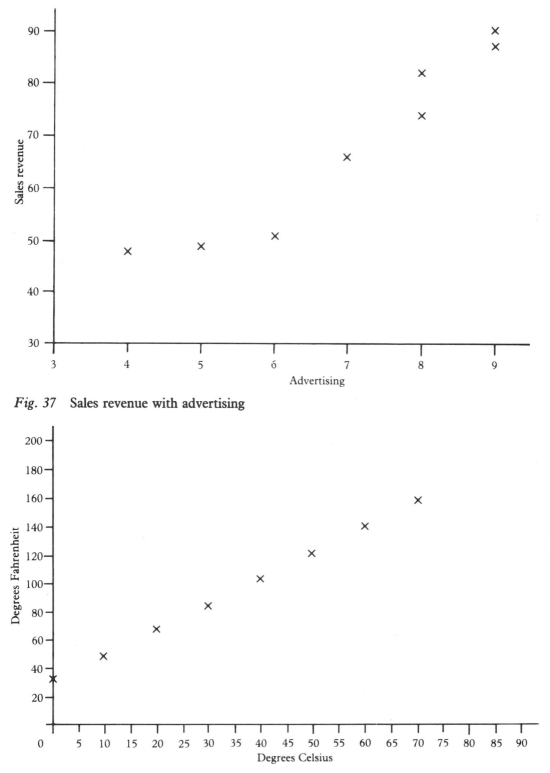

Fig. 37 Sales revenue with advertising

Fig. 38 Degrees Celsius v. Fahrenheit

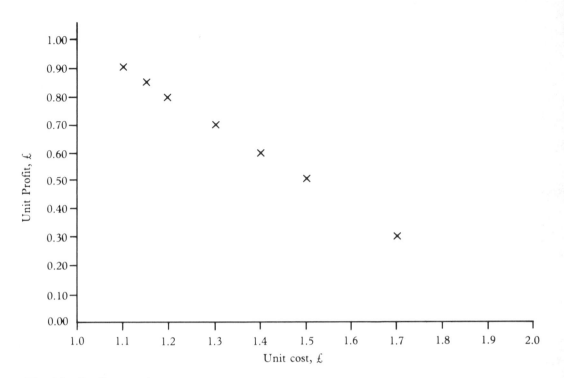

Fig. 39 Profit v. unit cost

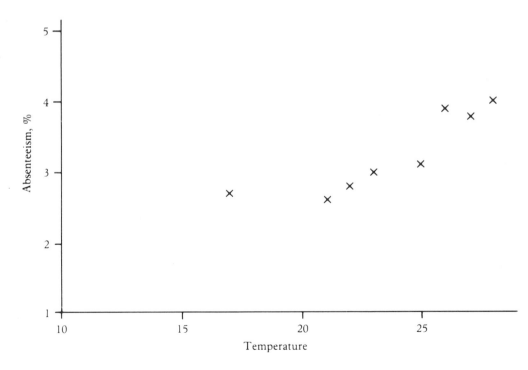

Fig. 40 Absenteeism v. temperature

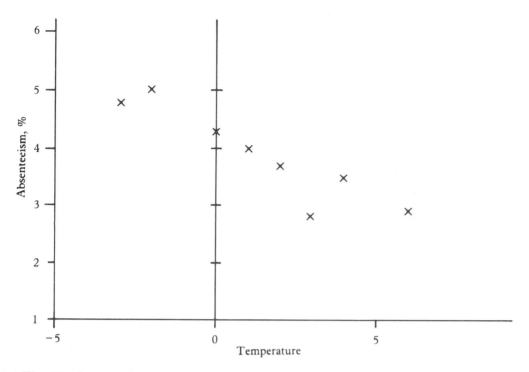

Fig. 41 Absenteeism v. temperature

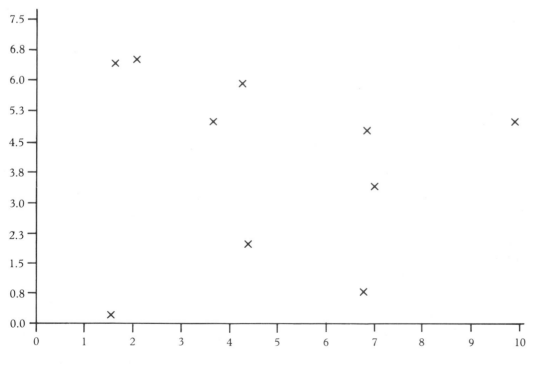

Fig. 42 Random numbers

result of mathematical laws. In this case we are looking at the relationship between degrees Celsius and degrees Fahrenheit. Figure 39 shows the perfect negative correlation between the profit and cost per unit of a component with a fixed selling price. The *y* variable (profit) falls in exact step with the increase in the *x* variable (cost). We are much more likely to be faced with the situations shown in Figs. 40 and 41, where we have an imperfect positive and negative correlation, respectively. Both show relationships between absenteeism and outside temperature. Figure 40 shows a positive correlation in summer (people are more likely to stay away when it is warmer) while Fig. 41 shows a negative correlation in winter (people stay at home if it is too cold). Figure 42 shows a situation where there is no correlation at all.

■ 6.3 THE CORRELATION COEFFICIENT

The correlation coefficient (Pearson's product moment correlation coefficient to give it its full name) is a statistic which measures how good the mathematical relationship between the two sets of data is. It can vary between $+1$, which means a perfect positive correlation (Fig. 38), and -1, a perfect negative correlation (Fig. 39). A value of zero means no correlation at all (Fig. 42). The sign ($+$ or $-$) of the correlation coefficient tells us whether the correlation is positive or negative (i.e. whether the graph slopes up or down from left to right).

This correlation coefficient is usually referred to as *r* and its value is given by the equation:

$$r = \frac{\Sigma(x - \bar{x})(y - \bar{y})}{N\sigma_x\sigma_y}$$

where *x* and *y* are the values of the *x* and *y* variables respectively, $\bar{x}$ and $\bar{y}$ are their means, σ_x and σ_y are their standard deviations and *N* is the number of pairs of data.

When we calculate *r* we usually use the following equation, which is derived from the above, but is much easier to calculate:

$$r = \frac{\Sigma xy - N\bar{x}\bar{y}}{N\sigma_x\sigma_y}$$

Let us illustrate its use by looking first at the correlation between advertising and sales revenue for Company X.

We need to construct a table as in Table 25.

We now calculate:

The mean of *x* (advertising expenditure) = 56/8 = 7.00
The mean of *y* (sales revenue)   = 547/8 = 68.38
The standard deviation of $x\sqrt{(\Sigma x^2/n - \bar{x}^2)}$ = 1.73
The standard deviation of *y*   = 16.32

We now have all the information we need to calculate the correlation coefficient so, substituting in the equation:

$$r = \frac{4046 - 8 \times 7 \times 68.38}{8 \times 1.73 \times 16.32} = 0.96$$

Table 25   Sales and advertising for Company X

Advertising expenditure (£000)	Sales revenue (£000)	Sales × advertising	Advertising × advertising	Sales × sales
5	49	245	25	2 401
9	90	810	81	8 100
9	87	783	81	7 569
8	82	656	64	6 724
7	66	462	49	4 356
8	74	592	64	5 476
4	48	192	16	2 304
6	51	306	36	2 601
Sum 56	547	4 046	416	39 531

Table 26   Sales and time for Company X

Month	Sales revenue (£000)	Sales × month	Month × month	Sales × sales
1	49	49	1	2 401
2	90	180	4	8 100
3	87	261	9	7 569
4	82	328	16	6 724
5	66	330	25	4 356
6	74	444	36	5 476
7	48	336	49	2 304
8	51	408	64	2 601
Sum 36	547	2 336	204	39 531

This confirms the evidence of Fig. 37 which shows that there appears to be a very close relationship between advertising expenditure and sales revenue.

If we apply the same procedure to sales revenue against time, we get the result shown in Table 26.

The mean of x (month) $= 36/8 =$ 4.50
The mean of y (sales revenue) $= 547/8 = 63.38$
The standard deviation of x $= 2.29$
The standard deviation of y $= 16.32$

Substituting in the equation we get:

$$r = \frac{2336 - 8 \times 4.5 \times 63.38}{8 \times 2.29 \times 16.32} = 0.18$$

This is not zero, but it is certainly quite close to zero, and we would be correct in concluding that the figures give no indication of an upward or downward trend in sales revenue.

Exercise 33
Now calculate the correlation coefficients for the following data, which is shown in Figs. 38 and

40. Check your results for the Fahrenheit to Celsius example before going on to the absenteeism example.

Table 27 Degrees Celsius versus degrees Fahrenheit

Celsius Y	Fahrenheit X	$Y \times Y$	$X \times X$	$X \times Y$
0	32			
10	50			
20	68			
30	86			
40	104			
50	122			
60	140			
70	158			

Table 28 Absenteeism versus temperature, summer

Temperature X	Absenteeism Y	$X \times X$	$Y \times Y$	$X \times Y$
26	3.90			
17	2.70			
23	3.00			
25	3.10			
21	2.60			
28	4.00			
22	2.80			
27	3.80			

In interpreting a correlation coefficient, a good rule of thumb is that anything between -0.7 and $+0.7$ is probably not worth taking too seriously. A correlation coefficient of 0.7 means that less than 50 per cent of the variance of y is explained by the correlation with x, and x is therefore not the major factor in determining the value of y.

■ 6.4 RANK CORRELATION

Quite often we do not have exact measurements to work with. This is particularly the case when looking at market surveys where we often ask for things to be put in order of preference (e.g. when choosing a restaurant, in what order of importance would you put the following: good food, clean, attentive service, comfortable, easy parking, quick service etc.?), or we only have very broad measures (e.g. age between 30 and 40, or salary between £10 000 and £15 000).

When we have ranked data we use a different, and much simpler, method of calculating the correlation coefficient. The coefficient we get is also slightly different although its interpretation is exactly the same. It is called **Spearman's rho**, after its discoverer, and is usually represented by R.

The formula is:

$$R = 1 - \frac{6\ \Sigma D^2}{N^3 - N}$$

where N is the number of pairs of values and D is the difference in rank of each pair.

To illustrate this, let us assume that we have carried out a survey in which consumers have put into order of preference eight attributes of a product. We have separately surveyed consumers in urban and rural areas and have got the results shown in Table 29.

Table 29   Ranking of product attributes

	Rank	
Attribute	*Urban*	*Rural*
A	2	1
B	3	3
C	1	2
D	5	5
E	7	6
F	8	7
G	6	8
H	4	4

We might wish to know if the preferences in urban and rural areas are close enough for us to ignore the differences. To calculate R we set up the problem as shown in Table 30.

Table 30   Calculation of R

	Rank			Difference
Attribute	*Urban*	*Rural*	*Difference*	*squared*
A	2	1	1	1
B	3	3	0	0
C	1	2	−1	1
D	5	5	0	0
E	7	6	1	1
F	8	7	1	1
G	6	8	−2	4
H	4	4	0	0
			Sum	8

When we substitute the value of ΣD^2 (= 8) in the formula, we get:

$$R = 1 - \frac{6 \times 8}{8^3 - 8} = 0.9$$

This shows a good correlation between the preferences of urban and rural consumers, and suggests that we could probably safely ignore the differences.

■ 6.5 INTERPRETATION AND USE OF THE CORRELATION COEFFICIENT

Correlation coefficients should be used with caution. All too often it is assumed that a high value of coefficient proves a relationship between the variables concerned. This is not so, all the coefficient shows is a **mathematical** association between the values. We must distinguish between **correlation**, which is purely mathematical, and **causation**, which is concerned with underlying mechanisms. A high value of correlation coefficient may well indicate a causal relationship but it does not prove it. For example, if we were to correlate house prices with average income, we would certainly get a good correlation, but does this mean that high house prices cause high incomes (people demand more so that they can afford to buy houses) or that high incomes cause high house prices (people can afford more so that demand pushes up prices), or that both are independent expressions of inflation?

Equally, a low value of correlation coefficient does not prove that there is no relationship, only that too many other factors are involved for us to get a clear picture (it took many years for the link between cancer and cigarette smoking to be clearly established because of the many other factors involved).

Before we use correlation we should establish that there is a reasonable mechanism for one of our variables to influence the other. It is not unreasonable to assume that advertising influences sales revenue, though it will not be the only influence, and if we wish to predict the level of sales that a given amount of advertising will result in, correlating sales revenue against advertising expenditure is a reasonable way forward. A high value of correlation coefficient (>0.7 or <-0.7) tells us that our prediction is likely to be accurate, while a low value (between -0.7 and 0.7) tells us that it will probably not be accurate enough to be worth considering. It does not tell us that advertising does not affect sales.

Since correlation is a purely mathematical technique, caution must be exercised when moving outside the range of values on which the coefficient is calculated. In the example of Company X, we have shown a good correlation between advertising and sales revenue for advertising expenditures between £4000 and £9000. We could probably assume that this would hold below £4000 and, perhaps, up to £15 000, but it would obviously be absurd to expect the same relationship to apply for advertising expenditures of, say, £90 000. The correlation applies to the figures we use and we go outside that range at our peril. However, we often have no choice but to go outside the range of our data, particularly when using correlation for forecasting, so the rule is to be more cautious in interpreting the figures the further outside the range you go.

Coincidence often gives very good correlations. We will see in Chapter 9 how we can test a correlation coefficient for coincidence, but the best defence is to start with a theory (e.g. advertising affects sales revenue) and then look for the evidence, rather than to look for correlations first and then try to explain them.

■ 6.6 SUMMARY

We have learned in this chapter that it is possible to calculate the mathematical relationship between two sets of data, and that this measure is called the correlation coefficient. We have seen two forms of the correlation coefficient, and considered the situations in which the coefficient might be used and the pitfalls we must beware of when using it. In the next chapter, on regression, we will see how, having established a good enough correlation, we can calculate predicted values of one variable from the other (e.g. what sales revenue should we expect from an advertising expenditure of £14 000).

■ 6.7 STUDY AND EXAM TIPS

  1 Always plot the points on graph paper. You will then be able to see if the coefficient should be positive or negative and whether you would expect a high or low value.

  2 Lay out the table as shown with columns for x, y, x^2, y^2 and xy. This will help you to go through all the steps correctly. Correlation is often associated with regression (see next chapter) and these values are needed for regression as well.

  3 You will not necessarily fail if you get a wrong answer, but you must check your answer against the graph and at least tell the examiner if you think it is incorrect (e.g. if the points slope up from left to right and you have a negative coefficient). Remember that you can never get a coefficient which lies outside the range -1 to $+1$.

■ SELF ASSESSMENT QUESTIONS

Answer the following questions and then check your answers against those at the end of the book. If you get any wrong, re-read the relevant parts of the chapter. If this does not help, then talk to your tutor about the problem.

  1 The correlation coefficient is:
(a) A measure of the effect of one variable on another
(b) A measure of the mathematical association of two sets of figures

2 A good correlation is shown by:
(a) A value of greater than 1
(b) A positive value
(c) A value between 0.7 and 1.0 or −0.7 and −1.0
3 The sign of the correlation coefficient shows the direction of the relationship.
(a) True
(b) False
4 Which correlation coefficient would you use for ranked data:
(a) Spearman's
(b) Pearson's?
5 A correlation coefficient of −1.5 is:
(a) Very good
(b) Impossible
(c) Very poor
6 A good correlation coefficient proves that there is a causal relationship.
(a) True
(b) False
7 The correlation will hold good over all possible values of the variables.
(a) True
(b) False

■ EXAMINATION QUESTIONS

(a) Describe how scatter diagrams and correlation coefficients can show the relationship between two associated sets of data. Illustrate your answer with examples from a business context. (8 marks)

(b) Eight types of cleaning fluid have been tested for their efficiency and then ranked in order with the most efficient being given rank one and the least rank eight. The results, together with the price of each one, are given below:

Fluid	Rank in order of efficiency	Price per litre in pence
A	4	86
B	1	88
C	5	58
D	3	74
E	2	76
F	8	60
G	7	70
H	6	55

(i) After ranking the price of each type of fluid, calculate the rank correlation coefficient between efficiency and price. (8 marks)
(ii) Interpret your answer to part (i) and comment on the data. (4 marks)
(Association of Business Executives 1987)

Over a period of time the consumer market for carpeting has been analysed and, among other things, various price changes (X per cent) and corresponding changes in sales (Y per cent) have been noted. The results are:

X%:	5	7	14	8	10	12	16	9
Y%:	14	19	8	10	9	11	4	12

Construct an accurate scatter diagram and calculate the product moment coefficient of correlation. Comment on the result.

(Institute of Marketing 1987)

Measurements are taken in an engineering workshop in order to establish whether there is a relationship between the speed of a moving part and its life.

Speed (rpm)	Life (hours)
16	146
18	137
21	135
21	129
23	115
25	118
26	109
29	101
31	97
32	83
34	85

Plot the data on a scatter graph and comment on the results.

(Institute of Commercial Management 1985)

A department store has information on a random sample of ten days of the number of people who enter the store and the number of people who use its restaurant.

Day	Enter store (000s)	Use restaurant (000s)
1	2.1	0.9
2	3.6	1.1
3	1.8	0.8
4	4.2	1.0
5	1.9	1.1
6	5.6	2.5
7	3.9	1.4
8	6.0	2.8
9	2.6	1.0
10	5.3	1.4

(a) Draw the scatter graph for the number of people entering the store against the number of people using the restaurant. (6 marks)

(b) Calculate the product moment correlation coefficient of the number of people entering the store and the number using the restaurant. (10 marks)

(c) Comment on what your answers to parts (a) and (b) show. (4 marks)
(Association of Business Executives 1988)

(a) Describe the difference between the product moment and the rank correlation coefficients and explain the circumstances in which one might prefer to use each of them. (10 marks)

(b) Research has been conducted into the percentage recall of advertising material among a panel of readers of daily newspapers. Members of the panel have also been asked to indicate their liking for each newspaper by placing them in order of preference. From the summary data that follows, comment upon the result. (10 marks)

Newspaper	Order of preference	% recall of advertisements
A	9	7.2
B	3	9.8
C	10	6.8
D	1	11.5
E	6	9.3
F	4	10.3
G	12	4.6
H	2	10.7
I	7	6.4
J	11	5.3
K	5	8.7
L	8	7.2

(Institute of Marketing 1987)

7 | Regression

■ 7.1 INTRODUCTION

When we have demonstrated that a statistical relationship, or correlation, exists between two variables, for instance advertising expenditure and sales revenue, it is extremely useful to be able to predict one from the other. What sales revenue will result from a particular level of advertising or, alternatively, what level of advertising is required to give a particular sales revenue?

The statistical technique of **regression** is used to determine the quantitative relationship between two variables, and invariably follows on from the establishment of a good correlation.

In this chapter we are going to look at the following aspects of regression.

In section 7.2 we will look at what a regression line is. In section 7.3 we will find out how to calculate a regression line. In section 7.4 we will look at the interpretation of the regression line, and at some of the problems which can arise.

■ 7.2 WHAT IS A REGRESSION LINE?

Figure 43 shows the sales revenue and advertising expenditure for Company X. If you were asked to draw a straight line through the points, you would probably produce something like that shown in Fig. 44, and we could treat this as showing the general relationship between advertising and sales.

Let us suppose we want to know what sales would result from an advertising expenditure of £7700. If we draw a vertical line from £7700 to our straight line, and a horizontal line from the point where they intersect, we can read off the sales revenue of £76 000 from the sales side of the graph. This is shown in Fig. 45.

There are two problems with this approach. The general problem that reading from graphs is always less accurate and less convenient than calculating a value, and the particular problem of whether or not the line we have drawn is actually the one which best fits the points on the graph. To overcome these problems we need to use the straight-line formula which has the following form:

$$y = ax + b$$

where x and y are our variables and a and b are constants. In other words, a and b always stay the same.

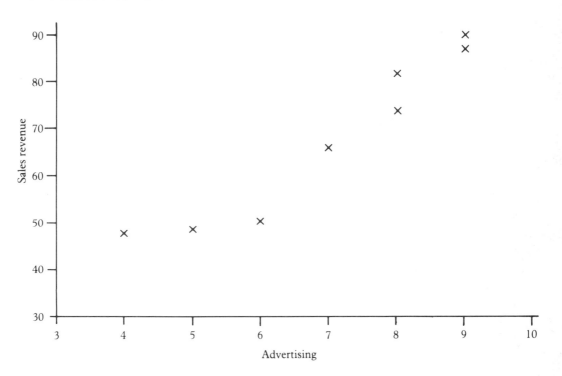

Fig. 43 Sales revenue with advertising

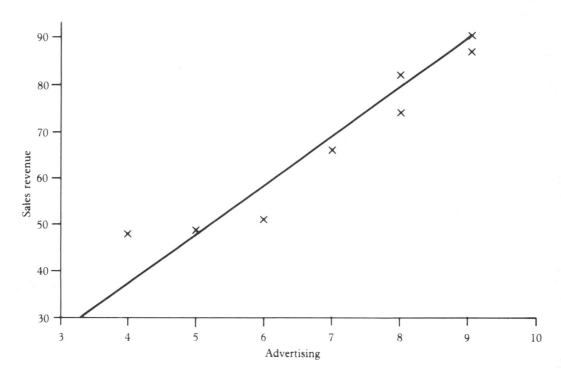

Fig. 44 Sales revenue with advertising

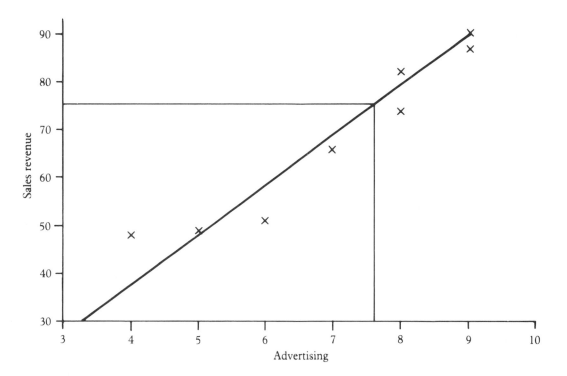

Fig. 45 Sales revenue with advertising

To illustrate the use of the formula, let us consider an example we are all familiar with, our electricity bill. This is made up of the following components:

> The **rental charge** for the supply to our home. This is the same regardless of how much electricity we use and is *b* in our formula.
> The **cost per unit** of electricity used. This is also the same regardless of the amount of electricity used and is *a* in the formula.
> The **number of units** of electricity used. This is variable and is *x* in the formula.
> The **total charge** for electricity. Another variable, *y* in the formula, and the value we wish to know.

In words we have:

Electricity bill = Cost per × Number of + Rental
                            unit   units used   charge

or in symbols:

> $y = a \times x + b$

If we know that the rental charge is £10 and the cost per unit is 10 pence we can work out the electricity bill for any number of units used. If we have used 1000 units the bill will be:

> $y = 10$ pence $\times 1000 + £10$

which is:

10 000 pence + £10

or   £100 + £10

thus our bill will be £110.

The difficulty with regression is, of course, that we do not know the values of *a* and *b*. We will look at their calculation in the next section.

■ 7.3 CALCULATING THE REGRESSION LINE

In calculating the regression line we are seeking to find the values of *a* and *b* which gives the smallest total difference between the points on the graph and the line (these differences are often referred to as **errors** since they represent the error that would arise if we used the value given by the regression line rather than the actual value). Figure 46 shows our graph of sales against advertising with these differences marked. Since some are positive and some are negative, they would cancel each other out if we just added them, so we square them first. Since we are trying to find the line which minimises the sum of the squared errors, this method is sometimes called the method of **least squares**.

There are three common ways of calculating *a* and *b*. These are best explained through examples, so we will calculate the regression line for the effect of advertising on sales revenue by each method. You will notice that in all three methods we are subtracting values. Since the differences between the values is

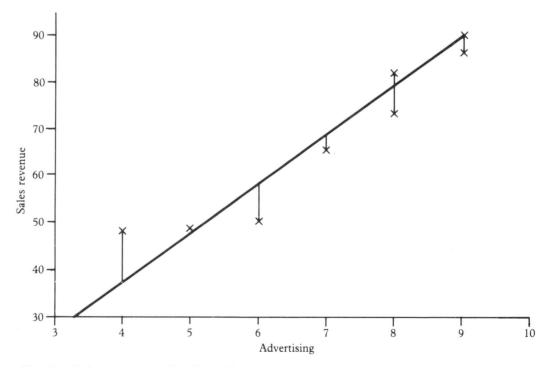

Fig. 46 Sales revenue with advertising

often quite small, it is important that we work to a precision of at least two decimal places more than that required in the answer.

7.3.1 Method 1

The following two simultaneous equations give the values of a and b which represent the line of best fit:

$$\Sigma y = nb + a\Sigma x$$
$$\Sigma xy = b\Sigma x + a\Sigma x^2$$

where n is the number of sets of values we have.

We first set up a table of values of x, y, xy and x^2 (Table 31).

Table 31 Sales and advertising for Company X

Month	Advertising expenditure (£000) X	Sales revenue (£000) Y	X × X	X × Y
1	5	49	25	245
2	9	90	81	810
3	9	87	81	783
4	8	82	64	656
5	7	66	49	462
6	8	74	64	592
7	4	48	16	192
8	6	51	36	306
Sum	56	547	416	4046

We now have $n = 8$, $\Sigma x = 56$, $\Sigma y = 547$, $\Sigma x^2 = 416$ and $\Sigma xy = 4046$. Substituting these values in the two equations, we get:

$547 = 8b + 56a$ and	(1)
$4046 = 56b + 416a$	(2)

Multiplying equation (1) by 56 and equation (2) by 8 we get:

$30\ 632 = 448b + 3136a$ and	(3)
$32\ 368 = 448b + 3328a$	(4)

If we subtract equation (3) from equation (4) we now get:

$$1736 = 192a \quad \text{or}$$
$$a = 1736/192 = 9.0417$$

Substituting this value of a in equation (1) we get:

$$547 = 8b + 506.3333 \quad \text{or}$$
$$8b = 547 - 506.3333 = 40.6667 \quad \text{and}$$
$$b = 5.0833$$

The equation of the regression line of sales revenue on advertising expenditure is therefore:

$$y = 9.0417x + 5.08333$$

7.3.2 Method 2

Rather than going through the process of setting up and solving simultaneous equations, we could derive formulae for a and b. The formulae look fairly daunting, but provided we take things one step at a time, are easy to use:

$$a = \frac{n\Sigma xy - (\Sigma x)(\Sigma y)}{n\Sigma x^2 - (\Sigma x)^2} \tag{5}$$

and

$$b = \frac{(\Sigma x)(\Sigma xy) - (\Sigma y)(\Sigma x^2)}{(\Sigma x)^2 - n\Sigma x^2} \tag{6}$$

You will see that these call for the same totals as the previous method, so we still have to set up Table 31.

Substituting the values from Table 31 in equation (5) we get:

$$a = \frac{8 \times 4046 - 56 \times 547}{8 \times 416 - 56 \times 56} \quad \text{or}$$

$$a = \frac{32\,368 - 30\,632}{3328 - 3136} = \frac{1736}{192}$$

which comes to 9.0417.

Substituting in equation (6) we get:

$$b = \frac{56 \times 4046 - 547 \times 416}{56 \times 56 - 8 \times 416} \quad \text{or}$$

$$b = \frac{226\,576 - 227\,552}{3136 - 3328} = \frac{-976}{-192}$$

which comes to 5.0833.

So again the regression line is:

$$y = 9.0417x + 5.0833$$

7.3.3 Method 3

This method is probably the simplest to calculate provided you have first calculated the correlation coefficient.

The equations for a and b are:

$$a = \frac{r\sigma_y}{\sigma_x} \tag{7}$$

$$b = \bar{y} - a\bar{x} \tag{8}$$

All of these values are calculated when calculating the correlation coefficient, and are (see Chapter 6):

$$r \ = \ 0.9598$$
$$\sigma_y = 16.3167$$
$$\sigma_x = \ 1.7321$$
$$\bar{y} \ = 68.3750$$
$$\bar{x} \ = \ 7.0000$$

Substituting in equation (7) we get:

$a = 0.9598 \times 16.3167/1.7321$ or
$a = 9.0415$

Substituting in equation (8) we get:

$b = 68.375 - 9.0415 \times 7$ or
$b = \ 5.0845$

So again we get a regression line:

$$y = 9.0415x + 5.0845$$

These three methods are mathematically identical and, as we have seen, give the same result (the very slight differences in the value of a and b is due to our working only to four decimal places). Which you use is a matter of personal preference, though in an examination it may well depend upon whether you are given a formula to use. My own view is that since you should never calculate a regression line until you have established that there is a good enough correlation, the third method will always be the easiest.

Exercise 34
Calculate the regression line for the following example using any (or all) of the three methods. If you have already done the examples in Chapter 6, you will recognise this. If you use method 3 you do not need to calculate the means, standard deviations and correlation coefficient again. Check your answer before going on to the second example.

Table 32   Degrees
Celsius v. degrees
Fahrenheit

Celsius	Fahrenheit
Y	X
0	32
10	50
20	68
30	86
40	104
50	122
60	140
70	158

Exercise 35
Calculate the regression line for the following example using any (or all) of the three methods. If you have already done the examples in Chapter 6, you will recognise this. If you use method 3 you do not need to calculate the means, standard deviations and correlation coefficient again.

Table 33   Absenteeism versus temperature, summer

Temperature X	Absenteeism Y
26	3.90
17	2.70
23	3.00
25	3.10
21	2.60
28	4.00
22	2.80
27	3.80

■ 7.4   INTERPRETATION OF THE REGRESSION LINE

The regression line is the line of best fit through a set of points. Figure 47 shows the data on sales and advertising for Company X again with our original line and the

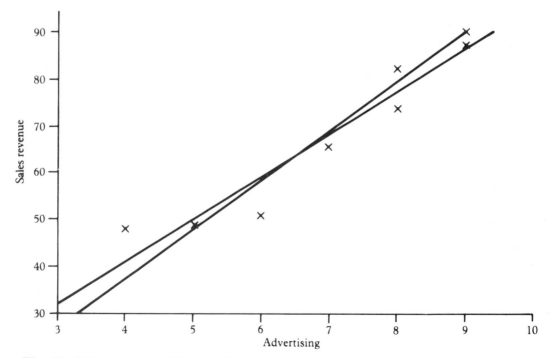

Fig. 47   Sales revenue with advertising

calculated regression line. We asked in section 7.2 what sales revenue would result from an advertising expenditure of £7700. The answer from the graph was £76 000. The answer from the regression equation is £74 704. This is possibly more accurate but the actual result could be quite different. We would not be too surprised to see a figure as low as £69 000 or as high as £81 000.

While a regression equation is always precise, its accuracy depends entirely on how good the correlation is, and with a correlation coefficient of between about −0.7 and +0.7 it is probably not worth considering.

The method of calculating the regression line minimises the error in y. The assumption is that we are trying to predict values of y from values of x. We must be sure that there is a reasonable mechanism by which x might influence y before we start, and we may certainly believe that advertising expenditure will influence sales. It is very unlikely that we would be able to say that sales influenced advertising expenditure in any one month, but we still might want to answer questions like 'what advertising expenditure is needed to give an average sales revenue of £70 000?' Unfortunately, we cannot answer this from the regression equation of y on x, since we are now trying to estimate x and so must use an equation which minimises the error in x. This is the regression of x on y and to calculate it we reverse all the references to x and y in any of the three methods. Using method 3 on the Company X data, we get the following results.

The regression line is $x = a'y + b'$

where $a' = \dfrac{r\sigma_x}{\sigma_y}$ \hfill (9)

and $b' = \bar{x} - a'\bar{y}$ \hfill (10)

As before:

$r = 0.9598$
$\sigma_y = 16.3167$
$\sigma_x = 1.7321$
$\bar{y} = 68.3750$
$\bar{x} = 7.0000$

Substituting in equation (9) we get:

$a' = 0.9598 \times 1.7321/16.3167$ \hspace{2em} or
$a' = 0.1019$

Substituting in equation (10) we get:

$b' = 7 - 0.1019 \times 68.375$ \hspace{2em} or
$b' = 0.0326$

and the regression line is

$x = 0.1019y + 0.0326$

We can now answer the question 'What advertising expenditure is needed to give an average sales revenue of £70 000?' by substituting 70 for y in this equation, and we get £7166. Had we used the regression equation of y on x, we would have got £7180 and, while the difference is not great, it illustrates the need to consider carefully what you are actually trying to find from a regression equation.

Great caution must always be used when extrapolating regression equations outside the range of the data on which they were based. For instance, in the case of Company X, the regression equation tells us that advertising expenditure of £30 000 will result in sales of £276 334. This is obviously very unlikely. The association of x and y may be just coincidence or, alternatively, the mechanism responsible for the association may apply only over a certain range of values. The examples of absenteeism versus temperature show a situation where the direction of the correlation changes at some temperature between 5 and 15 °C. Obviously, extrapolation here would be very dangerous (see Fig. 48).

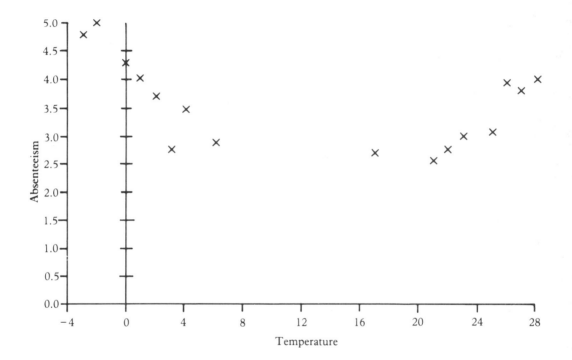

Fig. 48 Absenteeism v temperature

Even without extrapolation, the association may change. If another company entered into competition with Company X, sales would probably fall even though we kept advertising the same.

What we have considered in this chapter is, strictly, only **linear** regression. While probably the commonest and most useful form, situations do arise where the straight-line approach does not work well. Figure 49 shows the growth in capital of £1000 invested at 20 per cent per annum with the interest re-invested.

We could certainly calculate a line of best fit, but an equation which fitted the curve would be far more accurate. The field of **non-linear** regression is beyond the scope of this book, but you should be aware of the possibility when you draw a scatter graph.

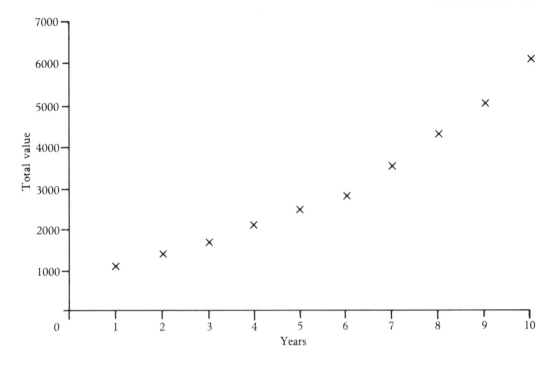

Fig. 49 Capital growth at 20 per cent

■ 7.5 STUDY AND EXAM TIPS

1 Because of the time available, an exam question may ask for a regression line without asking for a correlation coefficient first. Whether it does or not the following tips, also given in Chapter 6, apply.

2 Always plot the points on graph paper. You will then be able to see if the correlation coefficient should be positive or negative and whether you would expect a high or low value. If the graph slopes down from left to right, then you will get a negative value of a, while if it slopes up you will get a positive value.

3 Lay out the table as shown with columns for x, y, x^2, y^2 and xy. This will help you to go through all the steps correctly.

4 You will not necessarily fail if you get a wrong answer, but you must check your answer against the graph and at least tell the examiner if you think it is incorrect (e.g. if the points slope up from left to right and you have a negative value for a).

5 If there is an obvious curve to the points, mention that non-linear regression would probably be more appropriate.

6 If asked to extrapolate, always comment briefly on the risks of doing so.

7 Don't forget the need for precision in the calculations even if you round the answers to fewer decimal places.

■ SELF ASSESSMENT QUESTIONS

Answer the following questions and then check your answers against those at the end of the book. If you get any wrong, re-read the relevant parts of the chapter. If this does not help, then talk to your tutor about the problem.

1 The regression equation of y on x would be used to:
(a) Predict values of y from values of x
(b) Predict values of x from values of y
(c) Show that changes in x cause changes in y

2 The three methods of calculating the regression equation:
(a) Give different results and are used in different situations
(b) Give the same results

3 The regression equation of y on x:
(a) Minimises the total error
(b) Minimises the error in estimating y
(c) Minimises the error in estimating x

■ EXAMINATION QUESTIONS

Explain fully the meaning of the two terms 'Regression' and 'Correlation'. (10 marks)

Calculate the product moment coefficient of correlation for the following data which compares market penetration (y) and retail price mark-up (x) for a particular sector of manufactured products:

| x | 15 | 14 | 20 | 25 | 28 | 32 | 36 | 40 |
| y | 62 | 69 | 53 | 55 | 37 | 36 | 24 | 22 |

(10 marks)

(Institute of Marketing 1982)

An economist employed by a manufacturing firm is attempting to derive the demand function for one of its products. An analysis of the accounting records of the firm has produced the following data:

Price per unit (£ current purchasing power)	Demand (000s of units)
1.00	129
1.50	115
2.10	121
2.50	113
3.30	109
5.00	100

(a) Draw a scatter diagram depicting the above data. (5 marks)

(b) Calculate the regression of demand on price per unit. (13 marks)

(c) Hence estimate the demand for the product if the price per unit was £4.00. (2 marks)

(Association of Business Executives 1983)

You work in a marketing department of a medium-sized company producing music records and tapes. You have collected the following information over the past twelve months which shows for each corresponding month the number of complaints (Y) received by salesmen with the number of days lost through absenteeism (X) occurring in the quality control department.

X	14	8	12	18	4	16	2	9	15	11	7	21
Y	35	16	19	37	10	26	8	14	23	26	12	38

Find the equation of the regression line for Y on X and hence obtain the estimate of the probable number of complaints that will arise should absenteeism rise to a level of thirty days.

Comment upon the reliability or caution to be taken into account in giving your estimate.

(Institute of Marketing 1988)

The following information relates to the production of light commercial aircraft. Orders on hand and completions of aircraft are compared at the end of each quarter for the years shown.

Calculate the regression equation for the orders on hand depending on completions. Explain the purpose of the equation and estimate the orders on hand for six completions.

	1982				1983				1984			
Orders on hand	32	34	35	36	36	33	34	29	28	26	25	31
Completions	11	7	9	12	8	10	9	11	9	5	3	8

(Institute of Marketing 1987)

8 | Sampling

8.1 INTRODUCTION

We have seen in the preceding chapters how to display, manipulate and draw conclusions from statistical data, but we have not so far considered where this data comes from.

It is only very occasionally that we can say that we are dealing with all data. More usually we are dealing with data from a sample. In quality control, for example, we could weigh every bag of sugar we produce to check the accuracy of the bagging process, but this would be expensive and unreliable (how would we check the accuracy of the weighing process?). We would be far more likely to weigh only a sample of bags. If the measurement involved the destruction of the object (e.g. the breaking strain of a bolt) we have no alternative but to look at a sample. Most market research is entirely based upon samples since we could not possibly consult every customer.

In this chapter we will look at some of the more important issues involved in selecting and processing samples.

In section 8.2 we will briefly look at the principles and terminology of sampling. In section 8.3 we will look at the statistical behaviour of samples, and in section 8.4 we will consider some of the ways in which we can ensure that we get an accurate sample at lowest cost.

8.2 WHAT IS A SAMPLE?

There are two terms used in statistics which frequently cause difficulty, but which must be clearly distinguished if we are to avoid confusion. They are:

Population. The population, in statistics, is the whole of the data on all of the items of interest. For instance, if we are bagging sugar, it may be the weights of all bags of sugar ever produced or, more likely, the weights of all bags of sugar in the current batch. If we are conducting market research, it is the opinion of all possible customers for the product we are researching.

Sample. A sample is a number of objects selected from the population for measurement. We may look at every tenth bag of sugar, or seek the opinion of a preselected panel when doing market research.

We are usually concerned with means and standard deviations when dealing with samples, and the following terminology is used:

Sample mean $= \bar{x}$
Sample standard deviation $= s$
Population mean $= \mu$ (a Greek letter pronounced mew)
Population standard deviation $= \sigma$ (a Greek letter called sigma)

We take samples to save money. It is always cheaper to measure a sample than a population. Weighing bags of sugar may only cost a fraction of a penny per bag, but that is still a fraction of a penny off our gross profit, and over several million bags a year it may amount to a significant sum of money. In other fields the cost is much more substantial. The cost of destructive testing, which is common in all branches of engineering, is effectively infinite since, if we test the whole population, we have nothing left to sell. The cost of market and opinion research is also substantial since it involves the cost of staff employed solely to gather the data.

We are concerned with seeking to strike a balance between the cost of collecting the data and its value. Measuring the whole population may give us a more accurate and complete set of data (but how do you check the quality of your measurement?) but the much cheaper sample may give us as accurate a picture as we need.

We are never interested in the sample itself, but only in the sample as it reflects the population, so we are using the sample statistics as estimates of the population statistics. We are interested in $\bar{x}$ as an estimate of μ and s as an estimate of σ. The mathematics of samples is designed to tell us how accurate these estimates are, while the whole process of sampling is designed to ensure that we have a sample which is representative of the whole population. It is important that the way in which the sample is taken does not bias the outcome in some way.

■ 8.3   THE STATISTICS OF SAMPLES

8.3.1   Sample mean

Most often, when looking at sample data, we are interested in the mean of the population. Obviously, if our sample is the whole population, then the sample mean $\bar{x}$ will be exactly equal to the population mean μ, but as we reduce the sample size we might expect the $\bar{x}$ to become less and less accurate an estimate of μ. There is an important statistical rule which describes exactly the behaviour of sample means, the **central limit** theorem, and says:

The means of samples of the same size N, drawn from the same population, follow the normal distribution. This distribution has a mean equal to the population mean μ, and a standard deviation equal to the population standard deviation divided by $\sqrt{N}$ (i.e. $\sigma/\sqrt{N}$).

This is a very powerful rule, because it means that, regardless of the distribution of the population, we can apply the normal distribution to a sample mean, provided that:

The sample is representative.

The sample size, N, is greater than about thirty, or we have an independent measure of the population standard deviation.

As the sample size falls below thirty the distribution of sample means becomes less and less normal.

The central limit theorem does of course correspond with what we would expect, in that the means of samples tend towards the mean of the population, and the larger the sample size, the nearer the sample mean is likely to be to the population mean (the standard deviation of sample means, $\sigma/\sqrt{N}$, becomes smaller as N increases).

We cannot keep calling $\sigma/\sqrt{N}$ the standard deviation of the sample means and it is usually called the **standard error**.

Exercise 36
We have weighed every tenth bag from a sugar-bagging machine during the production of a batch of 500 bags. The mean weight is 1.021 kg, and we know from past records that the standard deviation of the process is 0.02 kg. What is the standard error of the sample?

We cannot, of course, deduce the population mean from the sample mean. Having taken a sample, we have no option but to assume that $\mu = \bar{x}$, but we can use the normal distribution to estimate the likely error in this assumption. As we know, the normal distribution is open-ended and there is never any value which we can say is theoretically impossible. If we were to say that our population mean lies between 1.00 and 1.061 kg, there would be a probability of being wrong. If we say it lies between 0.0 and 2.0 kg there is still a (very small) probability that we are wrong. We must be prepared to accept risk, and we must be prepared to specify the risk we will accept. This risk is specified by the **level of confidence** which is the probability that the true population mean will lie within the range we have assumed from the sample mean. It is specified as a probability (e.g. confidence level of 0.9) or a percentage (e.g. the 90 per cent confidence level). Common values are 90, 95 and 99 per cent.

You will have found, in exercise 36, that the standard error was 0.0028 kg. Let us say that we are prepared to accept a 10 per cent chance of being wrong in our estimate of the population mean. This corresponds to the 90 per cent confidence level. We now wish to find that range within which there is a 90 per cent probability of finding the population mean if the sample mean is 1.021 kg. We assume the population mean is 1.021 kg and then identify the area under the normal distribution curve corresponding to a 90 per cent probability. If we are concerned with establishing a range of the form $1.021 \pm x$, then we have the situation shown in Fig. 50, and we simply look up the z value for P of $(0.5 - 0.45 = 0.05)$ in the normal tables and find $z = 1.65$ (approximately). The range within which the population mean lies is therefore $1.021 \pm 1.65 \times 0.0028$ or:

$$1.021 \pm 0.0046 \quad \text{or}$$
$$1.0164 \text{ to } 1.0256$$

This range is called the **confidence interval**, and the particular range we have calculated is of course the 90 per cent confidence interval.

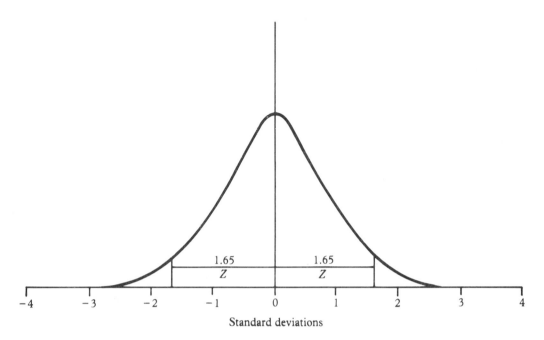

Fig. 50 Weight of bags of sugar

Exercise 37
What is the 95 per cent confidence interval for the mean weight?
If we had taken every fifth bag instead of every tenth, how would this change?

It is worth remembering that the 95 per cent confidence interval is $\bar{x} \pm 1.96$ standard errors, though this is often rounded up to 2. This may well be why it is one of the most frequently used confidence levels.

Quite often we are only interested in one end of the distribution. For example, if we are measuring the breaking strain of 10 mm bolts, we are concerned that they should not break below a certain figure, but we may not be interested in how much stronger than that they are. This makes a difference to the calculation of the confidence interval because we are only looking at one end of the normal distribution. This is shown in Fig. 51, and if we look up the 90 per cent confidence level in the normal tables we now get a z of 1.28, by interpolation, so the 90 per cent confidence interval becomes:

$$> \bar{x} - 1.28\sigma/\sqrt{N} \text{ as opposed to}$$
$$\bar{x} \pm 1.64\sigma/\sqrt{N}$$

Both of these are correct. Which we use depends upon the needs of the situation.

The minimum confidence level should always be decided first – do not let the data determine the risk that is acceptable. It is not logically defensible to lower the confidence level because the standard error is larger than expected.

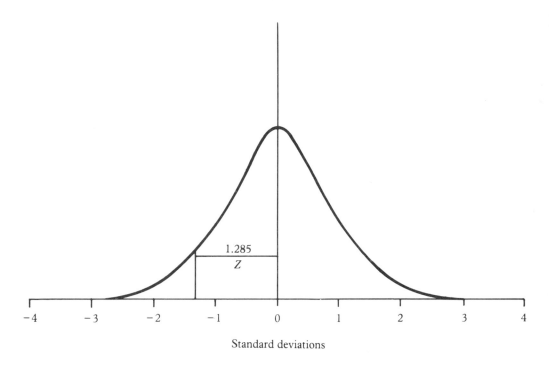

Fig. 51 Breaking strain of bolts

8.3.2 Sample standard deviation

In order to use the central limit theorem, we need to know the population standard deviation σ. As we have seen, this is sometimes available to us, particularly in quality-control applications where it can be found with reasonable certainty from the accumulated history of sample records, but often we only have the sample standard deviation.

The mathematician Bessel discovered that the sample standard deviation underestimates the population standard deviation by a small amount which varies with the sample size, and that a better estimate of σ is found by multiplying s by the Bessel correction:

$$\sigma = s\sqrt{N/(N-1)}$$

Exactly the same effect is obtained if we use the formula:

$$\sqrt{(\Sigma(x - \bar{x})^2/(N-1))}$$

rather than

$$\sqrt{(\Sigma(x - \bar{x})^2/N)}$$

when calculating sample standard deviations. Many calculators and computer packages do this automatically.

We should, then, either apply the Bessel correction or calculate the standard deviation using $(N-1)$ when using a sample to estimate the population standard deviation but, in practice, with samples greater than about thirty it makes no real difference and with samples below thirty the central limit theorem does not apply.

8.3.3 Samples of less than 30

When the sample size is less than thirty, the standard error does not follow the normal distribution but follows a very similar distribution called the *t*-distribution. This is broader and flatter than the normal distribution, and it gets broader still as the sample size gets smaller. There is, in fact, a separate *t*-distribution for each sample size.

A table of the *t*-distribution is shown in Appendix 4. The left-hand column is labelled 'degrees of freedom' for reasons which we do not really need to concern ourselves with. It is enough for the present to note that degrees of freedom = $N - 1$. Each column represents a particular probability, and the body of the table contains the number of standard errors. The example in the appendix is a very limited table and we must be prepared to make some approximations when using it, but it serves most purposes and more detailed tables are available if needed.

Let us imagine that we have noted the total expenditure of twenty customers, selected at random, over the past month, and have got the following results:

Mean $\bar{x}$ = £1374.56
Standard deviation s = £431.15
Estimate of σ = $s\sqrt{(N/(N - 1))}$ = 431.15 × $\sqrt{(20/19)}$ = £442.34
Standard error = $442.34/\sqrt{20}$ = £98.91

If we wish to find the 95 per cent confidence interval, we simply look down the column headed 5 per cent ($100 - 95$), at the row labelled 19 degrees of freedom ($20 - 1$), and we get a value of 2.09. The 95 per cent confidence interval is therefore:

£1374.56 ± 2.09 × 98.91

which is £1167.84 to £1581.28, but we would eliminate the quite spurious precision of this answer and say:

£1168 to £1581 or even £1150 to £1600

Exercise 38
We have weighed every twentieth bag from a sugar-bagging machine during the production of a batch of 500 bags. The mean weight is 1.021 kg. Since this is a new machine, we cannot assume that our past records of standard deviation apply. The standard deviation of the sample is 0.02 kg. What is the 95 per cent confidence interval? Compare this with the result of Exercise 37.

8.3.4 Binomial samples

Samples from the binomial distribution behave in exactly the same way as samples from any other distribution, but they are so common, particularly in market and opinion research, that they are worth special consideration.

We are invariably dealing with quite large samples, so the central limit theorem applies and we do not need to worry about corrections in the estimation of the population standard deviation.

Since we usually quote results from binomial samples as percentages, it is best to calculate the confidence interval on a percentage basis. Opinion research frequently operates at the 95 per cent confidence level, so we can simplify the process considerably by starting with a confidence interval of ± 2 standard errors.

Let us imagine that a local newspaper has commissioned an opinion poll on the outcome of a local election, and the result from a sample of 500 voters is 53 per cent supporting party X and 47 per cent supporting party Y. Can we go ahead and claim party X will win?

We know that the mean of the binomial distribution is Np and the standard deviation is $\sqrt{Npq}$. However, if we express the results in percentage terms, then the mean is simply P per cent and the standard deviation is $\sqrt{PQ}$ where P and Q are percentages rather than proportions. The standard error is, of course, $\sqrt{PQ/N}$ and the 95 per cent confidence interval is $P \pm 2\sqrt{PQ/N}$.

Substituting our values into this formula we get:

$$53 \pm 2 \times \sqrt{53 \times 47/500}$$
$$= 53 \pm 4.46 \qquad \text{or}$$
$$48.53 \text{ to } 57.46 \text{ per cent}$$

Obviously our sample is simply not accurate enough for us to conclude that X will win. We can improve accuracy by increasing the sample size and thus reducing the standard error.

If we want to say X will win, then we must have a sample large enough to reduce the confidence interval to less than ± 3 (i.e. so that the lower limit is still above 50 per cent). The requirement to find the minimum size of sample to give a given level of accuracy is so common that there is a standard formula for it. It is:

$$N = 4PQ/L^2$$

where N is the minimum sample size, P and Q the percentage probabilities and L the maximum error.

In the case of our opinion survey, we have:

$$N = 4 \times 53 \times 47/3^2 = 1107$$

We can now decide whether it is worth interviewing another 607 people to enable us to say that X will win (at the 95 per cent confidence level), but we should remember that the addition of a further 607 to our sample may well change the mean, and if the mean moves towards 50 per cent we still have not got a result.

Exercise 39
A sample of 1024 people have been asked which detergent they prefer: 37 per cent prefer brand A while 34 per cent prefer brand B, the remaining 29 per cent preferred a number of other brands, but none were preferred by more than 10 per cent. What is the 95 per cent confidence interval on brand A and brand B?

■ 8.4 TAKING SAMPLES

When taking a sample, the object is to obtain one that is truly representative of the population. It should also be large enough to give us the required accuracy in estimating the population statistics that we are interested in, but no larger since the larger the sample the more expensive the process of sampling and analysis. The defined population from which we take our sample is sometimes called the **sampling frame**. As we will see, this is not always the same as the actual population.

8.4.1 Simple random sampling

True random sampling is carried out in such a way that every member of the population is equally likely to be chosen as a member of the sample. This is the type of sampling we are using when we shuffle and cut a pack of cards (every card has an equal chance of being chosen) or toss a fair die, and while it seems to be quite simple and straightforward, it is actually very difficult to carry out in practice. If the population is clearly identifiable, and static, then we may use this method. For example, if we have just received a consignment of tins of paint from the manufacturer and wish to check a sample for quality, then if we numbered the tins in sequence we could use random number tables to choose a sample. The whole consignment would be our sampling frame.

Random number tables are tables of numbers carefully constructed so that there is no sequence or pattern in them. An example is shown in Appendix 7. to use them, we pick any point in the table as our starting point and then take the numbers in order (backwards or forwards, horizontally or vertically). If we started at the top left-hand corner of the table and worked from left to right, we would first take tin 94 followed by tins 79, 98, 30 etc.

This is an inefficient procedure, and we are much more likely to take a random starting point and then take every tenth tin (if the sample size required is 10 per cent of the population). This method is sometimes referred to as **systematic random sampling**.

A drawback with systematic random sampling is that the frequency of the sample may correspond with a natural cycle in the population. For example, if we are pressing tablets using a ten-stage rotary press, then every tenth tablet will be produced from the same die. In this case any sampling scheme based upon a multiple of 5 or 10 will not produce a representative sample.

Exercise 40
A social security office wishes to check a sample of 150 claimants' files. There are 3000 claimants' files in the office. How would you set about taking the sample?

Exercise 40 illustrates two problems that arise with any sampling scheme. One is to ensure that all the population is available for sampling. What do you do if file 137 is selected as part of the sample, but is in use, or lost, or misfiled? The other problem is to guard against human error (or inclination). If file number 2217 is chosen as part of the sample, but is very thick and would take a great deal of time to check, we may be tempted to take file number 2218 instead. This probably does not matter on one occasion, but the result of such bias in the long term is that difficult cases would always be under-represented. Such schemes need careful organisation and supervision.

Opinion polls are occasionally carried out by telephone. The telephone directory is a convenient sampling frame, with every subscriber listed, and it is not difficult to set up a sampling procedure. We could, for example, pick a starting page at random, then pick a number at random from every tenth page. The difficulty with this approach is that not everyone has a telephone and, unless we are sure that we only want the opinions of telephone subscribers, then our starting point misses out a large, and possibly important, part of the population.

8.4.2   Multi-stage sampling

This is a method of simplifying the selection of a relatively small sample from a large population. For example, if we wish to obtain a sample of households from across the country, we could conceivably obtain all the electoral registers for the country and sample from these. It is much simpler (and less expensive) to build up the sample in stages. First we would select a number of towns at random. For each town we would then select a number of streets at random, and from each street a number of houses. We now have our sample, but we have used much less information in producing it.

8.4.3   Cluster sampling

This technique is used when the population is widely dispersed and the information collection itself is expensive. It is commonly used when information needs to be gathered in an interview. If we wish to interview 1000 people selected at random over the country as a whole, it is obviously cheaper to interview 100 people in each of ten towns than to interview ten people in each of 100 towns. Our sample is composed of a number of discrete clusters. A similar approach might be used in a chain store seeking the opinion of its customers. Instead of sampling infrequently at all outlets, we could sample more frequently at a random selection of outlets. While the advantages in cost are considerable, we have reduced our sampling frame to a few locations among the many possible. Can we be sure that we have not missed important regional variations in doing so?

8.4.4   Stratified random sampling

Stratified random sampling (also known as **quota** sampling) is designed to increase the efficiency of random sampling by using prior knowledge. If we are trying to establish the opinion of the adult population about the amount of sports coverage on television, we might decide that the accuracy we require means a sample size of 1000. It is quite possible that when we select our random sample of 1000, we find that we have 544 men and 456 women, but we know that the population as a whole is 51 per cent women and 49 per cent men. It is generally believed that more men than women watch television sports coverage so our sample, although random, will produce a biased result.

The stratified sample overcomes this problem by identifying important characteristics whose distribution in the population is already known, and then sampling these groups separately. In the above example, we would take a random sample of 490 men and a random sample of 510 women and then combine the results.

Stratified sampling is widely used in opinion surveys and in market research where samples are frequently stratified according to sex, age, marital status and socioeconomic group. A market researcher in the high street may well be instructed to interview twenty married women aged between 20 and 30 in socioeconomic group C and having reached that quota, no more of the population in that category will be interviewed by that researcher.

If the data is gathered before the relevance of different population characteristics is known, or if we are using data gathered for another purpose, then the results of each group can be calculated separately and a weighted aggregate produced. This is less satisfactory than quota sampling but better than ignoring the problem.

8.4.5 Which method is best?

Strictly speaking, only simple random sampling gives a result which is bound to conform to the statistical rules which are considered in this and subsequent chapters. We have seen that even sequential sampling with a random start can introduce bias, and multi-stage and cluster sampling eliminate a large part of the population from consideration. It is, of course, inevitable that any attempt to reduce the cost of sampling carries the risk of reducing the accuracy as well, but in the fields of market and opinion research, the cost of the true random sampling would be prohibitive. Fortunately, the accuracy of multi-stage and stratified sampling has been well tested in these fields, and they can be used with confidence provided sufficient care is taken.

8.4.6 Collecting sample data

The most accurate and least expensive way to collect data is simply to count, provided we are only interested in a few readily identifiable characteristics. For example, a traffic census might count the number of cars, lorries and motor cycles passing a particular point in a day. This method is frequently used when trying to determine workloads and utilisation figures in factories and offices. Observations are taken according to a predetermined schedule, and the observer simply notes whether a machine is working or not, or whether a clerk is talking, writing, telephoning etc. In quality control, rather than measuring a particular characteristic of the component (its thickness, length, weight etc.) we check that it lies within a range using a simple gauge. The disadvantage with this approach is that it gives relatively little information. If we want to know that our sugar-bagging machine is correctly set, then we must weigh the sample of bags accurately, not just check that they are over 1 kg. This is a much more expensive activity which requires more skill, more time, and more sophisticated equipment. It is also more prone to error.

Opinion research poses special problems in data collection. Usually this is carried out using a questionnaire. Questionnaire design itself is a skilled task and the following observations represent only a brief outline of some of the more important points.

1 Questions should be brief and unambiguous. The respondent is likely to have forgotten the point of the question if it takes 5 minutes to read.

2 Questions should ask only one thing. Do not ask 'Do you think Brand X is cheaper and better than Brand Y?', but split it into two separate questions.

3 Avoid negatives. 'Do you agree that children should not be allowed into public houses?' is likely to be misunderstood by a significant proportion of respondents.

4 Keep the language simple. Questionnaire designers are usually of a higher educational level than typical respondents and sometimes forget the need for general comprehensibility.

5 Closed questions are easier to answer and easier to analyse than open questions. Asking 'What do you think of your local bus service?' invites lengthy, but not necessarily relevant, comment. It would be better to break the question down into several aspects and offer alternative answers for each, e.g.

> The local bus service is prompt:
> Agree strongly   ☐
> Agree   ☐
> Neither agree nor disagree   ☐
> Disagree   ☐
> Disagree strongly   ☐

This shows an example of a **Likert** scale, a simple but useful way of getting respondents to identify attitudes and preferences.

When using closed questions, make sure that all the alternatives are covered, or put in a catch-all option like 'other, please specify'. Bear in mind that too many options are likely to confuse the respondent and reduce the probability of a correct answer.

6 Lay out the questionnaire clearly. Give clear instructions on how it is to be completed and distinguish these from the questions in some way (e.g. a bolder type face). Clearly identify the space for the answers. Remember that someone will probably have to key the data into a computer for analysis, and accuracy here is just as important.

7 Do not have too many questions. A respondent may turn to the end first and seeing question number 74 will decide they do not have time to complete it. If the questionnaire is large, then use multipart questions with the separate parts identified alphabetically. The respondent is less likely to be deterred by seeing question 9f on the back page.

8 If it is important, define your terms. Don't ask about children or young people without specifying the age range. To someone of 80, young people might be 40 years old. Yesterday may mean different things to day workers and night workers.

9 Try to avoid predisposing the respondent. Do not say 'The government believes that ...... do you agree?' A large proportion of respondents will tend to agree because of the authority of the government, while a smaller proportion will disagree on principle. But the result will certainly be wrong. The question illustrated in paragraph 5 above would probably give rise to a quite different result if replaced by 'The local bus service is always late'.

10 Where the questionnaire is the basis of an interview, consider replacing

alternatives given on the document with show cards (these are cards containing numbered alternatives which the interviewer shows to the respondent). This gives a shorter and neater questionnaire which is cheaper and easier to process, but remember that the interviewer has to carry the show cards around and keep them in order.

Even with a well-designed questionnaire, the problems of data collection are only just beginning. The cheapest way of collecting data is to have the respondent complete the questionnaire in their own time and mail it to us. The questionnaire may be distributed by mail, as an insert with a magazine, or may be given out in shops or high streets. There are three obvious difficulties:

1 The response may not conform to the population profile we are interested in. This can be overcome by classifying respondents according to important features like age, sex etc. and building up a representative quota sample from the responses.

2 The respondents may not answer the questions accurately or truthfully. This is much more difficult to deal with. Some examples may be obvious and can be rejected immediately, although this means careful checking of each questionnaire. Good questionnaire design usually introduces a number of questions intended to check on the self-consistency of the answers. This will pick out some, but by no means all, of the inaccurate answers.

3 The response rate may be very low, depending upon the situation. In industrial market research, where we are dealing with relatively few, established, customers, a response of 80–90 per cent might be achieved. If the survey is sponsored by an organisation to which the respondents belong (i.e. a trade union, professional body etc.) and is obviously in their interests, a response of 60–80 per cent might be achieved, though not without at least two reminders to late respondents. In the case of random mail shots, or magazine inserts, the response may well be 10 per cent or less. While it is still easy to get a large enough sample, the real problem is that the sample is self-selected. We are only looking at volunteers, and they may very well not be representative of the whole population.

A frequently used means of overcoming these problems is the panel questionnaire. A preselected panel is periodically mailed a questionnaire. Because the panel has been selected with some care, they are more likely to be accurate and honest, and more likely to return the questionnaire. The selection process, usually involving interview, does add to the cost, and we are still dealing with volunteers who may not be representative.

The personal interview, based around a questionnaire, is probably the most accurate method available. This may be done on a door-to-door basis or in the high street. The trained interviewer can usually accurately classify the interviewee, and so build up the required quota efficiently, and can also identify inconsistent and inaccurate responses more readily. We should therefore get more accurate data. The bias introduced by using only volunteers is still present, but to a lesser degree since people are less likely to refuse a direct request for an interview. There are drawbacks even to this method. It will not sample motorists. The interviewer, usually female, is likely to be selective about whom she chooses, and the number of inebriated men in the sample is likely to be low. The way in which the questions are asked can well introduce bias, and on a cold wet winter's day there may be a temptation to invent data. Personal interview suffers from the same human failings as any other method.

None of these methods of gathering opinion data is completely satisfactory, and the better the quality of the data, the more expensive the method of collection. The above is a brief outline intended, as much as anything, to warn that this is not a field for amateurs.

■ 8.5 SUMMARY

In this chapter we have looked at the sample, the reasons for using samples, the means by which representative samples can be taken, and some ways of reducing the cost of sampling without sacrificing too much accuracy.

We have also considered the statistical behaviour of sample statistics, and introduced the central limit theorem and the concept of the confidence interval. We have used these to determine the quality of the sample statistics as an estimator of the population statistic, and have further shown how, given a desired level of accuracy, the required sample size (and so the cost) can be determined in advance.

In the next chapter we will look at further ways in which sample data can be used when the question is not 'What is the population?' but 'Does this sample come from an already known population?'

■ 8.6 STUDY AND EXAM TIPS

Questions of two types might arise:

1 Essay questions asking you to discuss particular aspects of sampling, or questions involving statistical calculations. Detailed questions about questionnaire design and market research and opinion survey methods are beyond the scope of this book. If they are likely to arise, your tutor will recommend appropriate reading to you. Questions about general principles of sampling, the statistical meaning of confidence etc. are likely to form only part of a question. Check the weighting given to the part and do not spend more time on your answer than that weighting justifies. Try and keep your definitions clear and concise, and always illustrate your answer with a simple example.

2 Statistical calculations, most probably on the confidence interval of the mean, or the minimum sample size required for a given accuracy.

2(a) How much data is there? If less than thirty values, use the t-distribution. If only normal tables are given, use the normal distribution.

2(b) Check whether the question is about one or both ends of the distribution. Sketch the normal distribution curve and mark the area of interest. This will help to ensure that you do not pick the wrong value of z.

2(c) If a confidence level is not given, 95 per cent is usually safe, but if it is an application where error is likely to be particularly expensive, for instance the nuclear industry, then 99 or 99.9 per cent may be better.

2(d) Look at your answer and ask if it looks reasonable. Confidence intervals are generally fairly small, and are not much use if they are large. If you obtain a large confidence interval, check that you have not misread or miskeyed the data.

■ SELF ASSESSMENT QUESTIONS

Answer the following questions and then check your answers against those at the end of the book. If you get any wrong, re-read the relevant parts of the chapter. If this does not help, then talk to your tutor about the problem.

1 In which of the following situations would you use a sample:
(a) Assessing the suitability of applicants for a job
(b) Testing the breaking strain of car windscreens
(c) Determining public support for a political party policy
(d) Determining the attitude of the management of a firm
2 The standard error is:
(a) The standard deviation of the population
(b) The standard deviation of the sample
(c) The maximum permitted error
(d) The standard deviation of the sampling distribution
3   The confidence level is:
(a) The range of the sample
(b) The chance of a value lying between specified limits
(c) The range within which the population statistic is likely to lie
(d) How confident you are that you have the right answer
4 The confidence interval is:
(a) The range of the sample
(b) The chance of a value lying between specified limits
(c) The range within which the population statistic is likely to lie
(d) How confident you are that you have the right answer
5 A random sample is:
(a) A sample where the members are chosen artibrarily
(b) A sample chosen in such a way that every member of the population has an equal chance of being chosen
(c) A sample chosen so that we cannot know in advance what will be in it

■ EXAMINATION QUESTIONS

(a) Discuss the advantages and disadvantages of the personal interview and the postal questionnaire as a means of collecting data. (10 marks)

(b) Describe what is meant by quota sampling and give an example of the type of survey for which it would be appropriate. (10 marks)

(Association of Business Executives 1987)

(a) What are the basic principles of good questionnaire design? (14 marks)

(b) Describe when you would use stratified sampling rather than simple random sampling. (6 marks)

(Association of Business Executives 1988)

A simple random sample of 35 stores in a chain gave the following sales figures in one particular week (in £000s):

191	143	171	190	197
194	159	198	215	239
232	181	220	238	241
228	277	155	254	199
191	200	190	145	187
186	243	242	226	249
162	187	217	203	154

Find the 95% confidence interval for the mean sales per week. If there are 120 stores in the chain, what is your estimate of the sales of the whole chain for the week?

(author's question)

(a) Discuss the advantages of collecting information by sample survey methods rather than by undertaking a complete census. (10 marks)

(b) What is meant by 'simple random sampling' and what are the principles upon which it is based? (10 marks)

(Institute of Marketing 1987)

Market research depends upon the collection of good statistical information. Compare and contrast any two of the most commonly used statistical sampling methods for collecting data, illustrating your answer where possible by reference to actual cases.

(Institute of Marketing 1985)

Write notes on **four** of the following:
(a) Questionnaire design
(b) Sampling frames
(c) Quota sampling
(d) Multi-stage sampling
(e) Interviewer bias

(Institute of Marketing 1987)

9 | Tests of significance

■ 9.1 INTRODUCTION

We have seen that we may take a sample to estimate an unknown population statistic. Quite often we already have some information about the population, and the reason for taking the sample is to test whether or not it comes from that population. For instance, when we set a sugar-bagging machine to produce bags with a mean weight of 1.04 kg, then the population mean that we require is 1.04 kg. We take a sample to test whether or not the population mean is 1.04 kg. We know what our average sales are. If we try a new promotional scheme, we might monitor sales to see if they have increased. In other words, we wish to know if our sample, the sales during the promotion, is from a population with a higher average. Situations such as this, where we have made a change and wish to see if it has had any effect on some statistic of interest, are one of the most important uses of statistics.

In this chapter we will look at the various ways in which we can test whether or not a sample belongs to a particular population, a field known as **hypothesis testing** or **significance testing**. In section 9.2 we will look at the definition of significance testing, and the procedures to be adopted. In section 9.3 we will look at the most important tests for the mean, while in 9.4 we will look at testing the standard deviation. In section 9.5 we will look at tests for changes in the pattern of the data, rather than for changes in specific statistics, while in 9.6 we will consider testing the correlation coefficient.

■ 9.2 THE SIGNIFICANCE TEST

Let us consider further the sugar-bagging machine. We believe that the machine has been set to produce bags with a mean weight of 1.04 kg, and we know that the process has a standard deviation of 0.02 kg. We are concerned about accurate setting here because if the machine is actually producing at less than 1.04 kg, then too many bags will come out at under 1 kg and we may be prosecuted for selling underweight bags. If the machine is producing at more than 1.04 kg, then our costs will be higher than necessary.

If we weigh a sample of thirty bags and get a mean weight of 1.034 kg what does this tell us? If we had made no assumptions about the population mean we would assume that the machine was producing at 1.034 kg with a 95 per cent confidence interval of $1.034 \pm 1.96 \times 0.02/\sqrt{30}$ or 1.027 to 1.041 kg.

This result illustrates the dilemma facing anyone trying to draw conclusions from statistical tests. Most of the 95 per cent confidence interval lies below our desired mean of 1.04 so it seems likely that the machine is producing at less than 1.04 kg, but 1.04 certainly lies within the 95 per cent confidence interval so we cannot rule out the possibility that the machine is set correctly. Whichever conclusion we come to, there is a possibility that we will be wrong. If we conclude that the sample is from a population with a mean of less than 1.04, then we should reset the machine to increase the mean weight. If our conclusion is wrong, then we are wasting sugar. If we conclude that the sample is from a population with a mean of 1.04, then we will leave the machine setting alone, and if we are wrong we will be selling underweight bags.

Statistical methods never prove anything but they can give precise indications of the balance of probabilities.

We do not use the confidence interval in significance testing, since it is too open to misinterpretation. Instead, we set up a procedure which identifies the most important type of error and allows us to specify the risk of that error that we are prepared to accept.

We always start by setting up the **null hypothesis**, which quite simply states that the sample **is** from the population in question. We then set up the **alternative hypothesis** which may be one of the following:

1 The sample is not from the population in question.
2 The sample is from a population where the statistic is greater than that of the population in question.
3 The sample is from a population where the statistic is less than that of the population in question.

Which alternative hypothesis we use depends on whether we are only interested in change, or whether we are interested in the direction of that change.

We now seek to disprove the null hypothesis, and if successful we then accept the alternative hypothesis. We do not attempt to prove the alternative hypothesis, since we cannot **prove** anything with statistical methods.

In the case of our sugar bags, the null hypothesis (often written as H_0) would be:

H_0: sample of mean 1.034 is from a population of mean 1.04

In this case we are equally concerned if the mean is greater or less than 1.04 so the alternative hypothesis (H_1) is:

H_1: the sample of mean 1.034 is not from a population of mean 1.04

If we can disprove H_0, then we accept H_1 and adjust the machine. There is, of course, always a risk that we have wrongly disproved H_0, and we must specify the level of risk we are prepared to accept. This is called the **level of significance** and is in this case the probability that a population of mean 1.04 could give a sample of mean 1.034.

Another way of expressing it is to say that it is the probability of wrongly rejecting the null hypothesis. This error is sometimes known as a **type 1 error**, or an error of the first kind, while the error of wrongly accepting the null hypothesis is a **type 2 error**, or error of the second kind.

If we consider our actions in the case of making either of these errors, we will see why the type 1 error is usually controlled in preference to the type 2 error.

If we wrongly conclude that the mean is 1.04, a type 2 error, then we do nothing except continue sampling, and eventually our sample will give a correct result and we will then adjust the machine. At worst we will have allowed a few underweight bags through the process.

If we wrongly conclude that the mean is not 1.04, a type 1 error, we will adjust the correctly set machine. It will now be out of adjustment, producing over, or under, weight bags, and when we next take a sample we will have to adjust the machine back again. Not only have we produced just as many rejects as when we made a type 2 error, we have incurred the cost of unnecessarily adjusting the machine twice.

The type 1 error is almost always more expensive than the type 2 error, and while we would ideally like to minimise both, the significance test is based upon minimising the former.

■ 9.3 SIGNIFICANCE TESTS OF THE MEAN

9.3.1 Test of one mean against a known population

The central limit theorem tells us that, provided the sample size is greater than thirty, the sampling distribution is normal with a mean equal to the population mean μ, and its standard deviation is the standard error $\sigma/\sqrt{N}$, where σ is the population standard deviation and N is the sample size.

This means that for a given population mean μ we can use the normal distribution table to find the probability of a sample mean $\bar{x}$ arising. If this probability is less than the level of significance we have chosen, then we can reject the null hypothesis.

Applying this to the sugar-bagging machine, we have an assumed population mean of 1.04 kg and a population standard deviation of 0.02 kg. The sample size is thirty so the standard error is:

$$0.02/\sqrt{30} = 0.00365$$

The null hypothesis is:

H_0: sample of mean 1.034 is from a population of mean 1.04

and the alternative hypothesis is:

H_1: the sample of mean 1.034 is not from a population of mean 1.04

If we decide on a 5 per cent level of significance, then we will reject the null hypothesis if the value of z lies outside the shaded area shown in Fig. 52.

Looking up 2.5 per cent (0.025) in the normal tables, we find it corresponds to a z of 1.96.

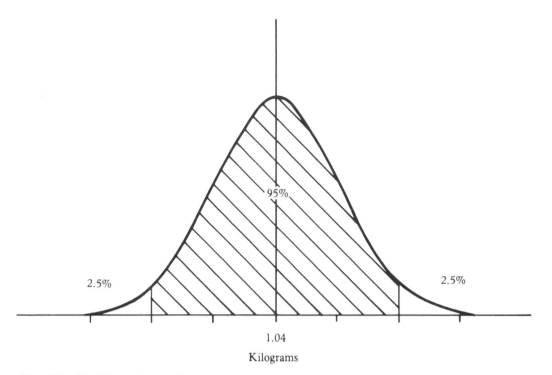

1.04

Kilograms

Fig. 52 Significance test of mean

The procedure is now quite straightforward. First, we calculate the limits outside of which we reject the null hypothesis. These are:

$\mu \pm 1.96\sigma/\sqrt{N}$ or
$1.04 \pm 1.96 \times 0.00365 = 1.033$ to 1.047

We now compare our sample result with these limits and if it lies outside, we reject the null hypothesis. The actual sample value lies inside these limits so we cannot reject the null hypothesis, but this does not mean that we necessarily accept it, only that we reserve judgement. If we add a further sample of thirty to the original sample, the limits would become:

$1.04 \pm 1.96 \times 0.02/\sqrt{60}$ or
1.0349 to 1.0450

and, if the sample mean remained the same, we could now reject the null hypothesis and reset the machine.

Note that we do not subtract the sample mean from the population mean, calculate z, and then look up a significnace level. We determine the appropriate significance level first. This makes the decision easy and avoids the temptation to change the rules to fit the data.

It can be convincingly argued that a z value of 1.96 is no more significant than a z value of 1.95 or 1.94 but, if we follow this line of argument, we end up with a z value of zero and no basis for decision. All limits are arbitrary, but establishing the limits first gets this argument settled at the beginning of the process.

Exercise 41
Company X sells mainly through personal visits to clients by its sales force. The mea.. order value per visit has been £145 with a standard deviation of £40. Difficulties with staff turnover have caused it to give new recruits a shorter and more intensive training course. The first 100 calls by new recruits gave a mean order value of £130. Has this changed the effectiveness of the sales force?

We are often interested in a change in only one direction. For example, we may introduce a new manufacturing process to increase the life of light bulbs. If the previous life was 1800 hours with a standard deviation of 220 hours, and a sample of fifty bulbs made by the new process gave a mean life of 2010 hours, have we improved the process?

H_0: life $\leq$ 1800
H_1: life $>$ 1800
Standard error = $220/\sqrt{50}$ = 31.11

If we use the 5 per cent level of significance, then, from the tables of the normal distribution, we find that 5 per cent (0.05) corresponds to $z = 1.645$. If our sample mean is greater than $\mu + 1.645$ standard errors, we reject the null hypothesis and accept the alternative hypothesis.

The limit is $1800 + 1.645 \times 31.11 = 1851.18$ so we reject the null hypothesis and conclude that the process has improved bulb life.

Where we are only interested in the difference, but not its direction, the test is sometimes referred to as a **two-tailed** test, since we are considering both tails of the distribution. When we are interested in differences in only one direction, we use a **one-tailed** test.

Exercise 42
Company X sells mainly through personal visits to clients by its sales force. The mean order value per visit has been £145 with a standard deviation of £40. The first 100 calls after a new advertising campaign gave a mean order value of £160. Has the campaign increased sales?

If the sample size is less than thirty we use the *t*-distribution as described in Chapter 8.

9.3.2   Test of two sample means

On occasion we may have the results of two samples with no prior knowledge of the population(s) that they have come from. The question here is usually whether or not they have come from the same population. To return to our light bulbs, a distributor may be considering two sources of supply for light bulbs. They may be equal in terms of cost and service, and the only remaining question is of quality. The distributor tests a sample of fifty bulbs from each supplier and obtains the following results:

Supplier	Mean	Standard deviation
A	1805	220
B	1923	230

Strictly, we should test the significance of the difference in standard deviations before looking at the means (see section 9.4) but it is small enough in this case for us to proceed.

For this test we again use the t-distribution, and t is given by:

$$\frac{\text{Difference between means}}{\text{Standard error of difference}}$$

or

$$\frac{\bar{x}_1 - \bar{x}_2}{\sqrt{((s_1^2 + s_2^2)/(N - 1))}}$$

where x_1 and x_2 are the two sample means, s_1 and s_2 are the two sample standard deviations, and N is the common sample size.

The degrees of freedom for this test is $(2N - 2)$.

Applying this to the example, we have:

$$t = \frac{1923 - 1805}{\sqrt{(220^2 + 230^2)/49}}$$

$$= \frac{118}{\sqrt{2067.34}}$$

$$= 2.6$$

The degrees of freedom are 98, which is near enough to infinity for the t-distribution, and the value of t for the 5 per cent level of significance is 1.96. Since our calculated value is greater than this, we reject the null hypothesis that the samples are from the same population and accept the alternative hypothesis that they are different and, by implication, that supplier B is superior.

The t test can be used where we have two samples of different sizes. The formula for the standard error of difference is a little more complicated, and is shown below:

$$\text{Standard error} = \frac{\sqrt{(N_1\sigma_1^2 + N_2\sigma_2^2)(N_1 + N_2)}}{\sqrt{(N_1 + N_2 - 2)/(N_1 N_2)}}$$

Exercise 43

Company X is evaluating the use of a training scheme for new assembly workers. Twenty-four new staff have been recruited, and twelve have been through a one-week training scheme, while twelve have had one week's experience on the shop floor. The results of their first week's work after this are:

	Mean output	*Standard deviation*
Trained	*435*	*44*
Untrained	*410*	*48*

Has the scheme made any difference?

■ 9.4   SIGNIFICANCE TESTS OF THE STANDARD DEVIATION

9.4.1   Test of one standard deviation against a known population

We do not often need to test standard deviations alone, but we should always be sure that the standard deviations of sample and population (or of two samples if that is the case we are dealing with) are not from different populations before using any of the tests for the mean.

One circumstance where the standard deviation is likely to be of more interest than the mean is where we are dealing with the tolerances produced by process equipment. Obviously a lathe or milling machine, or a sugar-bagging machine, which is able to produce to tight tolerances (i.e. a small standard deviation) is preferable to one which will only produce to a wide tolerance.

The standard error of the standard deviation is $\sigma/\sqrt{2N}$, where σ is the population standard deviation and N is the sample size. This behaves in exactly the same way as the standard error of the mean, i.e. it follows the normal distribution if $N > 30$ and the t-distribution if $N < 30$, so we can establish limits for levels of significance as shown in section 9.3.1.

Our present sugar-bagging equipment operates at a standard deviation of 0.02 kg. We are evaluating another machine, and on a trial of 100 bags it produced a standard deviation of 0.017 kg. Is it operating to a tighter tolerance? Note there is no mention of means in these figures, since the mean does not come into the calculations, but to make any sense, we must be comparing like with like, and both machines should have been set at 1 kg. The hypotheses are:

H_0: $s \geqslant \sigma$
H_1: $s < \sigma$

This is a one-tailed test and the value of z for the 1 per cent significance level is 2.325 (the 1 per cent level because this is an important investment decision, and to demonstrate that we do not always use the 5 per cent level).

Standard error $= 0.02/\sqrt{2 \times 100} = 0.0014$

The calculated value of z is:

$(\sigma - s)/0.0014 = (0.02 - 0.017)/0.0014 = 2.14$

This is less than the critical value of 2.325 so we must accept the null hypothesis. We have failed to prove that the new machine is superior at the level of significance we required.

Exercise 44
Company X sells mainly through personal visits to clients by its sales force. The mean order value per visit has been £145 with a standard deviation of £40. The first 100 calls after a new advertising campaign gave a mean order value of £160 with a standard deviation of £60. Are the standard deviation figures significantly different?

9.4.2   Tests of two sample standard deviations

This is probably the simplest statistical test of all, though it does involve yet another set of tables. It is known as the F-test, or variance ratio test. A table of probabilities for the F-test at the 5 per cent level is given in Appendix 5. If you wish to use other levels, then consult a book of statistical tables.

First we square our two standard deviations. This converts them into variances. Then we divide the larger variance by the smaller. The F table has columns headed 'Degrees of freedom of larger variance', and rows headed 'Degrees of freedom of smaller variance'. The figure to use in both cases is the sample size minus one.

Let us apply the F-test to the figures in Exercise 43:

Trained   : $s = 44$, $N = 12$, variance = 1936
Untrained: $s = 48$, $N = 12$, variance = 2304
The variance ratio F is 2304/1936 = 1.19
The degrees of freedom are $12 - 1 = 11$ for each sample

Looking at the table, we find it does not include a column for 11 degrees of freedom, so we must interpolate between 10 and 20 to get critical value of about 2.83. The calculated value of 1.19 is well below this so we accept the null hypothesis that the two samples came from populations with the same standard deviation.

Exercise 45
Company X is evaluating alternative suppliers for a component in its sugar-bagging machines. This component wears out during use and needs to be replaced periodically. Since it is much cheaper to replace the component during planned maintenance before it fails, consistency is almost as important as actual life expectancy. The following results have been obtained in tests:

Supplier	Mean life (hours)	Standard deviation	Sample size
A	124	18	17
B	121	12	20

Is product B superior in terms of consistency of life?

■ 9.5   TESTS FOR DISTRIBUTION OF DATA

We quite often find situations where neither the mean nor the standard deviation really tell us what we want to know. This applies particularly when we are dealing with classifications rather than measurements. For example, Company X sells three products. Records show that in the past month, sales have been as shown in Table 34.

Table 34

Product	North	South
A	120	240
B	180	175
C	195	220

Total sales in the south are greater, which is perhaps not surprising, but superficially it looks as if there are quite large differences in preference for the three products between the two regions. In this case, mean and standard deviation do not mean very much and we need a test that looks at the actual pattern of the data. This is the χ^2-**test** (pronounced Chi-squared). The statistic χ^2 is easily calculated as follows:

$$\chi^2 = \Sigma((O - E)^2/E)$$

where O is the observed value and E the expected value.

We already have a table of observed values. We need to construct a table of expected values, those expected on the basis of the null hypothesis that there is no difference in the preferences for the three products between north and south. First we calculate the row and column totals as in Table 35.

Table 35

Product	North	South	Total
A	120	240	360
B	180	175	355
C	195	220	415
Total	495	635	1130

Then we calculate the sales we would expect if the proportional sales of the three products in both the north and south exactly followed the proportional total sales. We do this by multiplying the column total by the row total and dividing by the grand total. The expected sales for product A in the north is:

$$495 \times 360/1130 = 157.7$$

Continuing this process, we get Table 36.

Table 36

Product	North	South	Total
A	157.7	202.3	360
B	155.5	199.5	355
C	181.8	233.2	415
Total	495	635	1130

Note that the row and column totals remain the same.
We can now set up a table showing the differences (Table 37).

Table 37

Product	North	South
A	−37.7	37.7
B	24.5	−24.5
C	13.2	−13.2

And finally a table showing $(O - E)^2/E$ (Table 38); χ^2 is the sum of these, 24.62. The χ^2 table is shown in Appendix 6. In order to use it we need the degrees of

Table 38

Product	North	South
A	9.01	7.03
B	3.86	3.01
C	0.96	0.75

freedom and the significance level we intend to use. The degrees of freedom for tabular data is:

$$(N - 1)(M - 1)$$

where N and M are the number of rows and columns respectively.

In our example, the degrees of freedom is $(3 - 1)(2 - 1) = 2$.

If we use a significance level of 5 per cent, then the critical value of χ^2 for 5 per cent and 2 degrees of freedom is 5.99. Our value of 24.62 is substantially greater than this and we must therefore reject the null hypothesis and accept the alternative hypothesis that north and south have different preferences.

The χ^2-test is subject to a number of limitations as follows:

1 Actual numbers must always be used. Never convert the data into percentages since this is equivalent to claiming to have 100 observations: if you have more than 100 observations, this reduces the sensitivity of the test; if you have less, then the result is valueless.

2 Expected values must always be greater than about 5. This may mean that adjacent groups must be merged to satisfy the rule. Alternatively, it may indicate the need for a larger sample.

Exercise 46
A holiday company gathered the folowing data from customers after holidays at three different resorts:

			Satisfaction	
Resort	*1*	*2*	*3*	*4*
A	10	55	74	30
B	35	30	24	5
C	20	44	30	2

where 1 is the highest satisfaction and 4 the lowest.
Is there any evidence that the resorts generated different levels of satisfaction?

■ 9.6   THE CORRELATION COEFFICIENT

We looked in detail at the correlation coefficient in Chapter 6 and saw that it was a measure of the degree of association between two sets of statistics. Even when a very high correlation coefficient is found, it is always possible that it arose purely by chance. Testing the significance of the correlation coefficient is designed to establish the probability that this is so. The significance level is the probability that the correlation is purely a chance event.

The correlation coefficient (we are here considering only the product moment correlation coefficient) follows the t-distribution, and t is calculated as follows:

$$t = r\sqrt{(N - 2)}/\sqrt{(1 - r^2)}$$

with $(N - 2)$ degrees of freedom. r is the correlation coefficient and N the number of pairs of data.

In Chapter 6 we looked at the relationship between sales revenue and advertising for Company X and found a correlation coefficient of 0.96 on eight pairs of data.

If we calculate t for this result we get:

$$t = 0.96 \times \sqrt{6}/\sqrt{(1 - 0.96^2)} = 8.4$$

If we enter the table of t at 6 degrees of freedom, we find the critical value of t at the 5 per cent significance level is 2.45. Our value is much greater than this so we reject the null hypothesis that the correlation is the result of chance and accept that it is significant.

Exercise 47
In Exercise 33 (Chapter 6) we calculated the correlation coefficient of absenteeism against temperature and got a coefficient of 0.8748 on eight pairs of values. Is this significant at the 5 per cent level? If so, is it significant at the 1 per cent level?

■ 9.7   LIMITATIONS OF TESTS OF SIGNIFICANCE

There are two linked difficulties is using any significance test. The fundamental difficulty lies in the fact that we are dealing with probabilities, not certainties. If you, or a firm, regularly carries out significance tests and uses the 5 per cent level, then five times out of 100 the result will be wrong. If tests are done 100 times a week, 250 mistakes a year will be made. The whole process of significance testing has been designed to make mistakes the least damaging, but this might still be considered unacceptable. Using the 1 per cent level reduces the error rate to only fifty per year, but makes clear decisions that much harder to obtain. One way of increasing the discrimination of the test (its ability to arrive at answers with a low error rate) is to increase the sample size, but this increases costs and may cause unacceptable delay.

One approach that is sometimes used is to gather the data, carry out the test, and then find out at what level the result is significant. We can illustrate this approach by looking again at the example of the sugar-bagging machine with the apparently smaller standard deviation. The original process gave a standard deviation of 0.02 and the new machine a standard deviation of 0.017 on a sample of 100. This gave a calculated z of 2.14. Originally we said the test should be carried out at the 1 per cent level, and since the critical vlaue of z was 2.325 we could not reject the null hypothesis. If, instead, we look up 2.14 in the normal table we get a probability of 0.016. In other words, we could reject the null hypothesis at the 1.6 per cent level of significance. We must now decide whether that is good enough. This approach can lead to creeping relaxation of standards (if 1.6 per cent is acceptable, why not 1.7 per cent etc.) and should, in the author's opinion, be avoided.

Some authorities take the view that if you can reject the null hypothesis at the 1 per cent level, then you should do so. If you cannot reject it at the 5 per cent level, you accept it and give up the exercise; while if you can reject it at the 5 per cent level but not at the 1 per cent level, take a further sample and try again. In effect we keep increasing the sample size until a clear decision is reached. This approach is probably the best compromise provided you can afford the time and resources to take further samples when it is indicated.

■ 9.8   SUMMARY

In this chapter we have looked at some aspects of what is probably the most useful application of statistics, tests of significance. We have seen how we can set up hypotheses and test them statistically in such a way as to minimise, and control, the probability of error. We have also seen how a fundamentally uncertain situation can be treated as if everything was definite by making the decision about level of significance in advance. We have looked at the application of the normal and t-distribution to decisions involving means, the normal, t- and F-distributions to decisions involving standard deviations, and the χ^2-distribution to decisions involving pattern. We have also considered the t-distribution with reference to the correlation coefficient. We have not by any means exhausted the topic of significance testing. There are many other situations, and many other tests. We have covered the most important and most commonly occurring situations and anything else is rare and requires the services of a professional statistician.

■ 9.9   STUDY AND EXAM TIPS

1 Read the question carefully to determine what sort of test is required. The most likely are sample mean and population mean, or two sample means. Are the sample sizes greater than thirty? Is it a z-test or t-test?

2 Sketch the distribution curve and outline the area of interest. Is it a one-tail or two-tail test?

3 Carefully define the null hypothesis and the alternative hypothesis. Make sure you get them the right way round (the null hypothesis broadly says that there is no difference between the two). Make sure they are expressed in a way which is consistent with your sketch.

4 Remember that you cannot **prove** anything in a significance test. This is a very common mistake in exam answers and it suggests a lack of understanding even when the mechanics of the answer are correct. All you can do is reject hypotheses.

5 Check your answer against common sense. If your two means or standard deviations or distributions look very similar, then you are unlikely to reject the null hypothesis except by mistake.

6 If the question involves comparing patterns, i.e. χ^2, construct the tabulation carefully and remember the rule of $E \geqslant 5$. The occasional E of 3 or 4 is probably acceptable, but Es of less than 1 certainly are not.

7 In the unlikely event that you are asked about the significance of a correlation coefficient, remember that a low coefficient is not very useful no matter how significant it is.

8 When choosing a significance level, explain why you have chosen it. Almost anything from 5 to 0.1 per cent can be acceptable but it must be justified; 5 and 1 per cent are probably the safest.

■ SELF ASSESSMENT QUESTIONS

Answer the following questions and then check your answers against those at the end of the book. If you get any wrong, re-read the relevant parts of the chapter. If this does not help, then talk to your tutor about the problem.

1 Which test is used for:
(a) Two sample means with a small sample size
(b) The correlation coefficient
(c) A sample mean and a population mean with a large sample size
(d) Two sample means with a large sample size
(e) The standard deviation of two samples with a small sample size
(f) The shape of a set of data?

2 The level of significance is:
(a) The chance of being right
(b) The accuracy of the result
(c) 95 per cent
(d) The risk of being wrong

■ EXAMINATION QUESTIONS

(a) A simple random sample of 425 camera batteries from a given production run shows that the mean life was 150 hours under normal use. If the sample standard deviation was 15 hours, what is the 95 per cent confidence interval of the mean life of all batteries in the production run? Could the true mean be as high as 160 hours? Explain your answer. Also test the hypothesis that the true mean is 148 hours or less, using the 1 per cent level of significance. (12 marks)

(*Institute of Marketing 1987*)

(a) The table shows the number of pints of milk purchased by a representative group of households during the month of July 1984. Calculate the arithmetic mean and the standard deviation for this grouped frequency distribution.

No. pints	No. households
15– 19	4
20– 29	7
30– 39	13
40– 49	19
50– 64	27
65– 79	16
80– 99	8
100–119	3
120–149	3

(12 marks)

(b) If the arithmetic mean and standard deviation for the previous month had been 67.5 pints and 20.3 pints respectively, compare and contrast the sales of milk for the two months. (8 marks)

(*Institute of Marketing 1985*)

A supermarket chain finds that in one of its stores, A, the mean amount spent by each customer is £12.50. A new sales promotion is adopted in all stores and subsequently a random sample of 125 customers at store A has a mean sales of £13.20 with a standard deviation of £3.25, and a random sample of 100 customers at store B has a mean sales of £13.50 with a standard deviation of £3.25.

(i) Test whether there is a significant improvement in sales value at store A after the promotion policy. State in your answer the significance level you are using. (10 marks)

(ii) Test whether there is a significant difference between mean sales value at stores A and B after the sales promotion. (10 marks)

(*Association of Business Executives 1988*)

(a) Distinguish between a one-tailed and a two-tailed test. (4 marks)

(b) A company which manufactures pocket calculators has invited tenders for the supply of batteries. Two large, well-established rival firms have tendered, and samples of batteries from both of these have been tested. A sample of 150 batteries from the first supplier had a mean life of 1643 hours with a standard deviation of 80 hours; a sample of 100 batteries from the second supplier had a mean life of 1671 hours with a standard deviation of 93 hours.

Test the following hypotheses at the 0.01 level of significance:

(i) The difference in the mean lives of the batteries is significant. (11 marks)

(ii) The batteries from the second supplier last longer than those from the first. (5 marks)

(Association of Business Executives 1983)

The size of motorcycles may be classified according to engine capacity thus:

<250 cc	small
250 cc and <550 cc	medium
550 cc and over	large

An organisation is interested in finding out whether there is any relationship between sex and preference for size of motorcycle and has investigated a random sample of 384 motorcyclists possessing full driving licences. Half the males in the sample purchased motorcycles of 550 cc and above while half the females purchased motorcycles of less than 250 cc. The remaining males in the sample split equally in purchases of small and medium-sized motorcycles but twice as many females had purchased medium-sized as large motorcycles. There were three times as many males as females in the sample.

(i) Summarise the above findings in tabular form and

(ii) Conduct a chi-squared test at the 0.01 level of significance to test the hypothesis that males prefer large motorcycles while females prefer small motorcycles.

(Association of Business Executives 1982)

10 Index numbers

10.1 INTRODUCTION

We have seen in previous chapters how to condense a mass of data into a few readily assimilated statistics as, for instance, the mean, standard deviation etc. There are circumstances where this simple approach, which in effect gives every member of the population an equal weight, does not give us the information we need. If we are trying to assemble a single statistic to cover a variety of different aspects of the subject, as in vendor rating for example, a simple mean is quite inappropriate. Equally, when we are looking at change, rather than absolute value, the actual numerical value of the statistic can obscure the information.

Most people would profess to some understanding of what a retail price index of 155 meant. If it was expressed in pounds it would have far less meaning.

In cases like this we use index numbers or indices. The units are generally abstract, i.e. they are just numbers, and are frequently referenced to some base value which represents an ideal or a starting point depending on the application.

In this chapter we will look at some of the more common types of index number and how they are constructed.

10.2 ARITHMETIC INDICES

This type of index is most commonly used when looking at changes in such things as prices, earnings, industrial output etc.

The simplest form of index is the simple average. For example, Company X sales for the years 1986, 1987 and 1988 are shown in Table 39.

Table 39 Company X sales (000s)

Product	1986	1987	1988
A	123	108	97
B	97	119	145
C	140	142	148
Total	360	369	390

To convert this into an index we first choose a **base** year, usually the earliest year, and we divide the base total into the other totals and multiply by 100. This gives us our index. The indices from Table 39, with base year 1986, become: 1986: 100, 1987: 102.5, 1988: 108.3.

Exercise 48
Calculate the indices for Company X sales with 1988 as base year.

We are frequently interested in both price, or cost, and quantity rather than just one or the other. The Retail Price Index (RPI) is a good example of a situation where a variety of different components in varying quantities and at varying prices are integrated into an index. We will illustrate its use with a simplified example (the full RPI is calculated on the basis of a comprehensive list of goods and services purchased by the 'average' household each week).

Let us imagine that the typical household purchases are as shown in Table 40.

Table 40　Household purchases

Potatoes	3 kg
Meat	1.5 kg
Bread	6 loaves
Milk	12 pints
Apples	1 kg
Cigarettes	10 packets

If we know the unit prices of these items in year x and year $x + 1$ we can calculate the total cost of the shopping basket as shown in Table 41.

Table 41　Cost year x and $x + 1$

		Year x		Year x + 1	
	Weight	Price (£)	Cost	Price (£)	Cost
Potatoes	3	0.20	0.60	0.23	0.69
Meat	1.5	3.30	4.95	4.20	6.30
Bread	6	0.50	3.00	0.55	3.30
Milk	12	0.24	2.88	0.27	3.24
Apples	1	1.10	1.10	1.05	1.05
Cigarettes	10	1.40	14.00	1.50	15.00
Total			26.53		29.58

If we establish year x as our starting point and give it a base value of 100, then subsequent figures are simply divided by the year x figure and multiplied by 100 to give the index.

In this case the index for year $x + 1$ is

$$29.58/26.53 \times 100 = 111.5$$

This particular index is based upon a fixed composition, the initial figures for quantity being referred to as the **base weights**, and as unit costs vary the index varies. It gives an absolute measure of change in price, but does not reflect changes in spending behaviour. If people stopped buying meat and bought more cigarettes instead, the index would not reflect this. Because we have chosen quantity as our weights, and are looking at the effect of price changes, this is a **price index**. We could equally have used prices as the weights, and looked at variations in quantity. Such an index is called a **quantity index**.

This type of index is called a **Laspeyres' index** (or sometimes **base-weighted index**) after the economist Laspeyres. It gives a true measure of price inflation but it does not reflect changes in the actual cost of living since it does not reflect changes in spending behaviour. If applied to earnings, it would give a true measure of earnings inflation for the individual, since it would be built by taking the average earnings and number of people employed in each category of employment, but the number of people employed in each category would then be assumed to remain constant, so changes in total earnings would be hidden.

Expressed mathematically, the Laspeyres' index is:

$$\frac{\Sigma p_i q_o}{\Sigma p_o q_o} \times 100$$

where p_o is the original unit price, q_o the original quantity and p_i the current unit price.

An alternative to the Laspeyres' index is the **Paasche index**, named after another economist. This index looks at both the current unit price and the current composition of the subject being indexed. It is also known as the **current weighted index**. Mathematically it is:

$$\frac{\Sigma p_i q_i}{\Sigma p_o q_i} \times 100$$

The Paasche index is more suited to circumstances where the composition changes fairly rapidly, but it is obviously much more difficult to maintain. With the Laspeyres' index we only have to track prices, with the Paasche index we have to track quantitites as well and be prepared to change the composition when necessary. If we applied a Paasche index to the RPI we would be looking not only at the change in the cost of items, but also at changing spending patterns in the population. The Paasche index would not give a reliable measure of price inflation on a year-to-year basis.

Governments generally use the Laspeyres' index for RPI comparisons because it is much easier to maintain and because it does give a reasonable measure of price inflation, but the need arises periodically to revise the composition of the shopping basket as it becomes too out of step with people's actual behaviour. Provided that indices with both the old and new weights are published for at least one period, it is easy to convert any figure from one base to the other.

Since neither index offers a perfect measure of price change when both price and quantity are changing, some authorities recommend an average of the two as the most satisfactory measure.

A disadvantage with both indices is their tendency to appear to overstate the rate of change. For example, if the RPI rose from 221 to 243 over one year, it appears to have risen by 22 points, but prices have actually only risen by 10 per cent (22/221) in fact. As indices get older they get too far from their starting point to be easily understood. There is a case for restarting indices when this happens. The chain-linked index, in which each year is indexed only against the previous year, overcomes this particular problem, but does not allow comparison from year to year, or over a number of years, against a fixed base.

Exercise 49
Calculate the Laspeyres' and Paasche price indices for the following data, using 1985 as the base year. Quantity is in 000s and price in £:

Sales of four products

Product	1985 Price	1985 Qty	1986 Price	1986 Qty	1987 Price	1987 Qty
A	9.5	11.0	9.8	12.4	11.3	10.2
B	2.7	15.5	3.2	17.8	3.4	22.1
C	4.4	27.0	4.5	18.0	4.1	11.2
D	8.4	2.1	7.0	12.0	6.5	17.5

■ 10.3 GEOMETRIC INDICES

Arithmetic indices are not appropriate when we are concerned with percentage change rather than the absolute value of a change. Consider the examples shown in Tables 42 and 43. In both cases we are constructing an index based on five share prices. In Table 42 a low-valued share has shown a large percentage rise while in Table 43 a high-valued share has shown a small percentage rise. Because the actual value of the rise in Table 43 is greater, it has had a greater effect on the index.

Table 42 Index of five share prices

Company	Price 1986	Price 1987
A	1.10	1.10
B	0.90	1.35
C	9.50	9.50
D	4.00	4.00
E	2.00	2.00
Sum	17.50	17.95
Index	100.00	102.57

Table 43 Index of five share prices

Company	Price 1986	Price 1987
A	1.10	1.10
B	0.90	0.90
C	9.50	10.50
D	4.00	4.00
E	2.00	2.00
Sum	17.50	18.50
Index	100.00	105.71

This index obviously does not give us a clear idea of the rate of growth.

The geometric index, based upon the geometric mean, does. In this particular case we multiply together the five prices for 1986 and take the fifth root, giving the geometric mean of 2.37. We then do the same for the 1987 figures which gives us 2.57 in the first case and 2.42 in the second. We obtain the index by dividing the new mean by the base mean and multiplying by 100. Table 42 now gives us an index of 108.45 while Table 43 gives an index of 102.02, which is a much better reflection of the rate of change.

This index is generally used as the basis for share indices such as the *Financial Times* Industrial Share Index. It has only one serious drawback and that is the effect of shares tending towards zero. A value of zero in any component of the index makes that index zero. It is occasionally necessary to remove the shares of troubled companies from the index for this reason.

■ 10.4   OTHER INDICES

Almost anything that can be expressed numerically can be converted into an index. The numerical expressions need not even be measurements, but can be ranks or even subjective assessments. Often the idea is to simplify the task of choosing between alternatives by reducing quite complex situations to a simple number. There is obviously risk in this, and such procedures must be used with caution.

A situation where this approach may be used is vendor rating, where we are concerned to rank alternative suppliers as a basis for choosing between them. First we would identify the relevant factors in a supplier's performance and attach numerical weights to these in proportion to their importance to us. We might end up with something like the situation shown in Table 44.

Table 44   Vendor quality factors

Factor	Weight
Product quality	7
Price	6
Delivery speed	4

This is not an exhaustive list but illustrates the sort of factors that are important. The weights are assigned from 1 (very little importance) to 10 (very important). We now establish a similar scale to measure vendor performance by each of the factors we have identified as important. Again it must be a scale of say 1 to 10 so that we have a consistent basis for comparison. We cannot simply multiply the delivery time by 4 and the price by 6. If we had established the performance measures for two vendors as in Table 45, we would compute the indices by multiplying the performance by the weight and summing the products.

On this basis we would prefer vendor B since their better price and delivery performance outweighs their poorer quality. Such systems can be useful but obviously great care must be taken in setting up the weights. Quite small changes in the example could give rise to completely different results.

Table 45   Vendor rating index

Factor	Vendor A Performance	× Weight	Vendor B Performance	× Weight
Quality	7	49	5	35
Price	6	36	8	48
Delivery	4	16	6	24
Index		101		107

■ 10.5   SUMMARY

We have seen that index numbers are a useful means of reducing a large mass of data to a single value for the purpose of comparison. They should be used with caution since they can oversimplify. We have looked at the construction and use of the two most common forms of index, Laspeyres and Paasche, and the geometric index for situations where rate of change is important rather than the absolute value of the change. We have also considered the possibility of setting up rather more subjective indices for other situations.

■ 10.6   STUDY AND EXAM TIPS

1 Careful reading of the question and careful arithmetic are the key issues. Make sure you understand the type of index you are being asked to calculate.

2 If the base year is not clearly stated, then use the earliest year given.

3 In a multipart question, look at the balance of the marks and try to allocate your time accordingly. Calculation is usually required before discussion, but try to leave enough time for at least a sentence of discussion.

4 Wide variations in index are unlikely in an exam. Index values of 10 or 1000 should be viewed with suspicion and lead to a careful check on your arithmetic.

■ SELF ASSESSMENT QUESTIONS

Answer the following questions and then check your answers against those at the end of the book. If you get any wrong, re-read the relevant parts of the chapter. If this does not help, then talk to your tutor about the problem.

1 The index usually used for RPI is the Laspeyres' index:
(a) True
(b) False
2 Which index uses current weights:
(a) Laspeyres
(b) Paasche
(c) Geometric?
3 The geometric index is used when we are interested in percentage change.
(a) True
(b) False
4 Which index is best for measuring price change only:
(a) Laspeyres
(b) Paasche
(c) Geometric?

■ EXAMINATION QUESTIONS

An importer of coffee beans notes the following changes in the prices and relative quantities of the five leading varieties marketed through his company. Results are quoted for the three-year period 1983 to 1985.

	1983		1984		1985	
Variety	Price	Quantity	Price	Quantity	Price	Quantity
A	3.65	7	4.00	6	4.13	5
B	2.14	9	2.37	11	2.35	12
C	2.85	8	2.89	10	2.98	8
D	3.29	12	3.38	15	3.52	18
E	4.06	6	4.23	6	4.11	7

Using 1983 as the base year:
   (a) Calculate the overall base-weighted price index for 1984 and also for 1985. (8 marks)
   (b) Calculate the overall current weighted price index for 1984 and also for 1985. (8 marks)
   (c) Using the results obtained in (a) and (b) to illustrate your answer, contrast the Laspeyres and Paasche methods for obtaining price index numbers. (4 marks)

(Institute of Marketing 1988)

The following table relates to wages paid to labour at two points in time.

	1975		1982	
Grade	Number	Weekly wage	Number	Weekly wage
A	200	18	190	48
B	175	23	140	60
C	110	24	100	62
D	94	26	103	62
E	266	31	358	72
F	24	38	42	84

(a) Calculate a base-weighted index of the wages paid using the aggregate method: (1) for 1982 using 1975 as the base and (2) for 1975 using 1982 as the base.

(b) Account for the infrequent use of current weighted indices. Have they any advantages and if so what are they?

(Institute of Commercial Management 1985)

The data below gives the quantities sold and the prices of the products of a firm manufacturing toiletries:

	1986		1987	
	Quantity	Price	Quantity	Price
Product	*(000s)*	*(p/unit)*	*(000s)*	*(p/unit)*
Skin lotion	110	85	115	95
Deodorant	345	120	380	130
Shampoo	520	70	604	90

(a) Calculate a price index which will represent the average price change in the firm's products. Describe the type of index you have chosen. (8 marks)

(b) Calculate the quantity index for the firm's sales in 1987 with base year 1986. Describe the type of index you have chosen. (8 marks)

(c) Comment on what the indices you have calculated show. (4 marks)

(Institute of Marketing 1988)

11 Forecasting

■ 11.1 INTRODUCTION

Among the most widely used statistical techniques are those concerned with attempting to predict the future. The relevance of this in business is self-evident. If we can predict future sales, we can ensure that our production capacity and purchasing arrangements match these, and thus maximise utilisation, customer satisfaction and profits. If we can predict machine breakdowns or labour absenteeism, we can take steps to minimise their impact on production. If we can predict competitors' behaviour, we can take steps to minimise the impact it will have on us. Unfortunately there are no techniques available to us that will accurately forecast all of these. Even if they were available they would also be available to our competitors and this may well cancel any advantage. There are, however, a number of techniques which produce forecasts of sufficient accuracy to be useful in a variety of situations, and we will look at some of the simpler ones in this chapter.

There are three broad classes of forecasting methods in use:

1 **Time series** methods which seek to extend past quantitative data into the future. For example, if sales have been rising by 2 per cent per month, we might assume that this will continue.

2 **Causal methods** which endeavour to construct mathematical models linking causes to effects. For example, we might believe that sales are linked to average earnings and therefore use average earnings as a predictor of sales.

3 **Subjective methods** which depend upon opinion as much as quantitative data. These methods, including scenario construction and Delphic polls, are used for planning corporate strategy, and sometimes for forecasting demand for low-volume high-value capital equipment. Being non-mathematical, they are beyond the scope of this book.

In section 11.2 we will consider a number of the simpler approaches to time series forecasting including moving averages and seasonal factors. In section 11.3 we will look at linear regression in the context of both time series and causal models.

■ 11.2 TIME SERIES FORECASTING

This is probably the area of forecasting with the greatest number of alternative techniques. All of them are attempts to distinguish between trends in the data and random variations or noise. By definition, random variations cannot be forecast so a good technique ignores it.

A difficulty which all techniques share is that of distinguishing between random variation and changes in trend. A single figure which is off the main line of the trend may just be noise, two consecutive figures may indicate a change. Techniques which are sensitive to change tend to be too sensitive to noise, while techniques which give a smooth forecast are usually slow to respond to a change in trend. The skill frequently lies in getting the sensitivity right.

We are going to consider only a few of the simplest techniques. If you are interested in pursuing the subject further, there are many books available and your tutor will guide you if required. It should be stressed that most time series techniques are rather more demanding, mathematically, than those we are going to consider.

11.2.1 The moving average

This is the simplest mathematical forecasting technique available. It balances following trends with ignoring random variation by averaging the data over the immediate past and using this average as the forecast. Table 46 illustrates a three-month and six-month moving average on the same set of data.

Table 46 Moving average of sales

		Actual moving average	
Month	*Sales*	*3-month*	*6-month*
Jan	100.00		
Feb	103.00		
Mar	120.00	107.67	
Apr	112.00	111.67	
May	111.00	114.33	
Jun	109.00	110.67	109.17
Jul	132.00	117.33	114.50
Aug	133.00	124.67	119.50
Sep	126.00	130.33	120.50
Oct	144.00	134.33	125.83
Nov	135.00	135.00	129.83
Dec	139.00	139.33	134.83

The three-month average is obtained by summing the last three months' sales and dividing by three. The six-month average is obtained by summing the last six months' sales and dividing by six. Each month, we drop the oldest figure from the total and add the newest, continuously updating the forecast. At its simplest, the latest moving average is the forecast for the next period.

These figures are shown in Fig. 53. We can see that both forecasts produce a much smoother line, clearly identifying the upward trend. The six-month average,

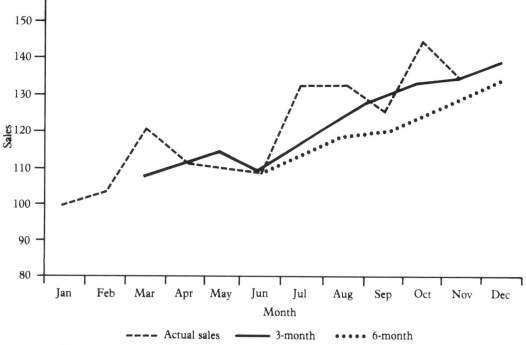

Fig. 53 Moving average of sales

as we might expect, is smoother than the three-month average. The sensitivity of moving average forecasts is adjusted by increasing or decreasing the period over which the average is calculated. We must remember that the moving averages are the basis for forecasting the next period's sales, and it is quite obvious from the graph that both lag behind the trend, the six-month average by more than the three-month average. This is, of course, due to the fact that the three-month moving average is an average based around the middle of the three months, and the six-month average is based around the mid-point of the third and fourth months. The former lags by 1.5 months and the latter by 3 months.

Exercise 50
Calculate the three-month moving averages for the following data.

Month	Sales
Jan	7.5
Feb	7.8
Mar	6.3
Apr	8.2
May	7.0
Jun	7.0
Jul	6.4
Aug	6.7
Sep	6.3
Oct	4.5
Nov	5.9
Dec	6.2

11.2.2 The *Z* chart

The *Z* chart is not strictly a forecasting technique, though it does clearly show trends, but is a method of displaying data which depends upon the use of a close relative of the moving average, the moving total. It is generally used to display annual sales, but it can equally be used to display weekly or monthly sales. If used for shorter periods than one year, the period should be long enough to absorb any seasonal effects.

Three figures are plotted on the same graph, the actual sales, the cumulative sales and the twelve-month moving total sales. The technique is illustrated in Table 47 and Fig. 54; the characteristic shape of the graph gives the technique its name.

Table 47   *Z* chart for Company X

Month	Sales 1985	Sales 1986	1986 totals Moving	1986 totals Cumulative
1	13.00	15.00	163.80	15.00
2	12.50	13.60	165.80	28.60
3	14.20	13.20	166.90	41.80
4	15.50	16.10	165.90	57.90
5	11.00	14.50	166.50	72.40
6	13.10	11.00	170.00	83.40
7	15.00	14.70	167.90	98.10
8	16.80	17.20	167.60	115.30
9	13.90	17.00	168.00	132.30
10	12.00	16.90	171.10	149.20
11	12.80	18.30	176.00	167.50
12	14.00	16.40	181.50	183.90

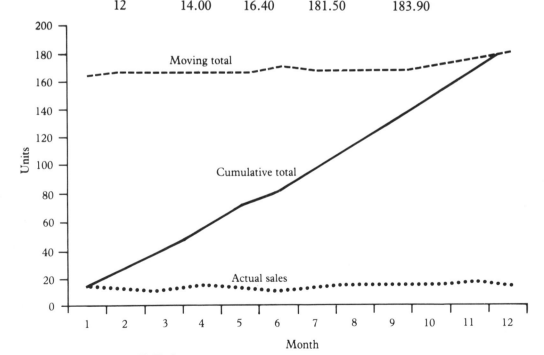

Fig. 54   Company X Z-chart

11.2.3   Trend and seasonality

The simple moving average is of direct use in forecasting only if we are sure that all variation is random. If there is a trend or any **seasonality** in the data, we must allow for these. We may use the moving average to extract any underlying trend in the value being forecast, and to extract any seasonality. Demand, in particular, often shows a pattern of variation which may be repeated from day to day (demand for electrical power or public transport show clear peaks and troughs at the same times each day), week to week (a great deal of general consumer demand is concentrated on Fridays and Saturdays), or year to year (holidays, new cars, etc.). If we can separate any underlying trend from the seasonal effects, then we are in a position to make a forecast for any time period. The term **seasonal** is sometimes reserved for patterns which repeat on an annual basis, and the term **cyclical** is used for patterns which repeat over other time periods.

In order to extract trend and seasonality, an approach sometimes called **decomposition** because we are decomposing the overall pattern into its component parts, we need data covering several cycles. It is easier to illustrate the process than to describe it, so we will establish the trend and seasonal factors for the data shown in Table 48.

Table 48   Company X sales

Year	Quarter	Sales (£K)
1985	Spring	203
	Summer	247
	Autumn	195
	Winter	172
1986	Spring	236
	Summer	255
	Autumn	190
	Winter	188
1987	Spring	245
	Summer	290
	Autumn	222
	Winter	192

In this particular case, we are looking at an annual pattern of demand, with quarterly sales figures. We could equally carry out the process with monthly sales figures – it would simply increase the amount of computation threefold.

There are two common methods for trend extraction:

> The regression method, sometimes called the least squares method, which we will look at in section 11.3.
> The moving average method, which we will consider now.

First we calculate a set of moving averages which are based on a period just long enough to eliminate the seasonal effect. In this case we must use a one-year moving average. Next we take the differences between these moving averages. Since we

Table 49 Company X sales, moving average

Year	Quarter	Sales (£K)	Moving average	Difference	Moving average
1985	Spring	203			
	Summer	247			
	Autumn	195			
	Winter	172	204.25		
1986	Spring	236	212.50	8.25	
	Summer	255	214.50	2.00	
	Autumn	190	213.25	−1.25	
	Winter	188	217.25	4.00	3.25
1987	Spring	245	219.50	2.25	1.75
	Summer	290	228.25	8.75	3.44
	Autumn	222	236.25	8.00	5.75
	Winter	192	237.25	1.00	5.00
			Average	4.13	

have eliminated the seasonality by taking a long enough period for the moving average, and eliminated much of the random variation by using an average, this is the trend (per quarter in this example). The process is shown in Table 49, and the results are shown graphically in Fig. 55.

Fig. 55 Company X sales

The trend figures shown in the fifth column probably still contain some random variation. We can reduce this by taking a moving average of the trend itself as shown in the sixth column and use this to forecast trend, but we have now used almost two years' data to get this far.

The idea of trend may seem fairly obvious, but there are several alternative uses of the term in time series analysis. In Table 49, we have treated trend as the rate of change in the base sales per quarter, and we have measured it in £K; we could have treated it as a percentage. Instead of saying sales are increasing by £4.13K per quarter, we could say that sales are increasing by X per cent per quarter. Which is used probably makes little difference if the rate of change is small, but could be important if the rate of change is large. The best method is selected by trial and error.

Trend is sometimes used to describe the deseasonalised figures, in other words the actual sales, or whatever, after we have removed the seasonal component. While this use of the term is acceptable if we are interested only in describing the past, it is of little use in predicting the future.

To extract the seasonal component we need a trend value which can be used on all the data, and the simplest value is a simple average. This is found to be £4.13K per quarter.

Using this trend we now adjust each sales figure to a base of spring 1985 by subtracting the cumulative effect of the trend (i.e. we subtract 4.13 from the second figure, 2×4.13 from the third and so on). This is shown in Table 50.

Table 50 Company X sales, trend adjusted

Year	Quarter	Sales (£K)	Adjusted sales
1985	Spring	203	203.00
	Summer	247	242.87
	Autumn	195	186.74
	Winter	172	159.61
1986	Spring	236	219.48
	Summer	255	234.35
	Autumn	190	165.22
	Winter	188	159.09
1987	Spring	245	211.96
	Summer	290	252.83
	Autumn	222	180.70
	Winter	192	146.57

We can now work out the seasonal factor for each quarter by calculating the mean adjusted sales and then calculating the mean percentage variation of each quarter from that. The percentage variation is found by subtracting the mean adjusted sales from the adjusted sales for that period, dividing the result by the mean adjusted sales and multiplying by 100. This is shown in Table 51.

What this tells us is that, on average, spring sales are 7.42 per cent above the base figure, summer 23.61 per cent above, autumn 9.81 per cent below and winter 21.2 per cent below.

Table 51   Company X seasonal factors

Year	Sales (£K)	Adjusted sales	Spring	Seasonal factors (%) Summer	Autumn	Winter
1985	203	203.00	3.11			
	247	242.87		23.37		
	195	186.74			−5.14	
	172	159.61				−18.93
1986	236	219.48	11.49			
	255	234.35		19.04		
	190	165.22			−16.08	
	188	159.09				−19.19
1987	245	211.96	7.67			
	290	252.83		28.43		
	222	180.70			−8.21	
	192	146.57				−25.55
Mean	196.87		7.42	23.61	−9.81	−21.22

An alternative method of extracting seasonality is shown in Table 52. This does not depend upon extracting trend first, and if the trend is slight or very variable, it is probably preferable. We again start with a four-quarter moving average, but we next calculate the average of adjacent pairs of moving averages as shown in column 4. Since the first moving average represents the point midway between summer and autumn, and the second the point midway between autumn and winter, the average of the two corresponds exactly to the autumn sales without seasonality or random variation. The difference between this and the actual sales, as a percentage, represents the seasonal factor for that period.

The results are quite close. The differences are due in part to the fact that the second method effectively eliminates a whole year from the calculation, but also due to the fact that the first method assumes a constant trend. If trend is variable, the second method is to be preferred; if it is fairly constant, then the first is probably better.

Table 52   Company X seasonal factors

Year	Sales (£K)	Moving average	Average of averages	Seasonal factor
1985	203			
	247			
	195		208.38	−6.42
	172	204.25	213.50	−19.44
1986	236	212.50	213.88	10.34
	255	214.50	215.25	18.47
	190	213.25	218.38	−12.99
	188	217.25	223.88	−16.02
1987	245	219.50	232.25	5.49
	290	228.25	236.75	22.49
	222	236.25		
	192	237.25		

This gives us:
Spring   7.92 per cent
Summer   20.48 per cent
Autumn   −9.71 per cent
Winter   −17.73 per cent

To use this for forecasting, we must first consider that a four-period moving average always lags by two periods. To forecast the sales for spring 1988 we take our latest moving average of 237.25, add two trend values to it to overcome the lag, and a further trend value to forecast the next period:

Base sales for spring 1988 = 237.25 + 3 × 4.13 = 249.64

We now make the appropriate seasonal adjustment:

Forecast sales, spring 1988 = 249.64 + 7.42 per cent = 268.16

Exercise 51
What are the forecast sales for autumn 1988?

Exercise 52
Forecast demand for the first quarter of 1988 from the following data:

Quarter	1985	1986	1987
1	22	24	25
2	41	53	60
3	36	55	52
4	18	27	32

11.2.4 Exponential smoothing

A potential disadvantage of the moving average is that it gives equal weight to the oldest and most recent figures in the average, and no weight at all to figures older than the time period of the average. It seems more reasonable to gradually reduce the contribution that a figure makes to the forecast as it gets older, so that the most recent information has the greatest effect.

The **exponentially weighted moving average**, more usually referred to simply as exponential smoothing, does exactly this and is surprisingly easy to use. Unfortunately it does not necessarily produce better results.

The formula for the exponentially weighted moving average is:

$$F_{t+1} = \alpha A_t + (1 - \alpha)F_t$$

where F_{t+1} is the forecast for period $t + 1$, F_t is the forecast for period t, A_t is the actual figure for period t, and α is the exponential coefficient, $0 > \alpha < 1$.

Since every actual is incorporated into the forecast and is multiplied by $(1 - \alpha)$ every period, the contribution of each figure diminishes with age, but never completely ceases.

The larger the value of α the more sensitive, and less smooth, the forecast. α is usually kept below 0.1 in practice. Table 53 shows the use of exponential smoothing on the same data as we used in Table 46, while Fig. 56 shows the result in graphical form.

The lag is very much greater in both cases, but if you compare Fig. 53 with Fig. 56 you will see that the forecasts are much smoother. An exponentially smoothed

Table 53 Exponential smoothing

Month	Actual Sales	$\alpha = 0.05$	$\alpha = 0.1$
Jan	100.00	100.00	100.00
Feb	103.00	100.15	100.30
Mar	120.00	101.14	102.27
Apr	112.00	101.69	103.24
May	111.00	102.15	104.02
Jun	109.00	102.49	104.52
Jul	132.00	103.97	107.27
Aug	133.00	105.42	109.84
Sep	126.00	106.45	111.45
Oct	144.00	108.33	114.71
Nov	135.00	109.66	116.74
Dec	139.00	111.13	118.96

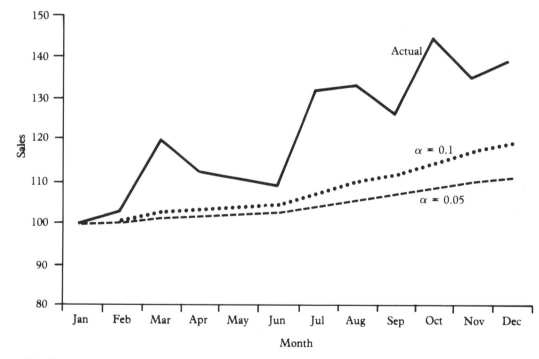

Fig. 56 Exponential smoothing

forecast with an α of 0.1 is very nearly equivalent to a simple weighted average of ten periods, so a lag of about five periods should be expected.

Exercise 53
Calculate the exponentially weighted moving average for the data in Exercise 50 using an α of 0.1.

11.3 REGRESSION

We have covered regression fully in Chapter 7 and will not go over the mathematics of the technique now. It is an obvious method to use when trying to forecast linear trends and, since regression lines minimise the squared error, it is sometimes referred to as the method of least squares.

We can use regression to extract the underlying trend when there is a seasonal pattern, but we must also extract the seasonal component to build a complete forecast.

If we calculate the regression line of sales per quarter for the data in Table 49, we will be able to compare regression with the moving average as a means of extracting trend.

In order to carry out a regression calculation, we first need to number the quarters consecutively. We then need to calculate the correlation coefficient and the standard deviations of the two variables. This is shown in Table 54.

Table 54   Regression of Company X sales

Year	Quarter	Period number	Sales (£K)
1985	Spring	1	203
	Summer	2	247
	Autumn	3	195
	Winter	4	172
1986	Spring	5	236
	Summer	6	255
	Autumn	7	190
	Winter	8	188
1987	Spring	9	245
	Summer	10	290
	Autumn	11	222
	Winter	12	192
Sum		78	2 635
Mean		7	220
Sum of squares		650	592 265
Σxy		17 365	
σ		3.45	33.74

$$r = \frac{\Sigma xy - N\bar{x}\bar{y}}{N\sigma_x\sigma_y} = 0.17$$

We can now calculate the constants for the equation $y = ax + b$ where y is sales and x is period number:

$a = r\sigma_y/\sigma_x = 0.17 \times 33.74/3.45 = 1.66$
$b = \bar{y} - a\bar{x} = 220 - 1.66 \times 7 = 208.38$

a is the trend, and is somewhat higher than the value of 1.03 that we obtained using the moving average.

We would now proceed exactly as we did in Table 51 to extract the seasonal factors. To produce a forecast we would use the regression equation:

$$y = 1.66x + 208.38$$

and then add the seasonal adjustment.

This example has shown the use of regression to extract a trend on a purely statistical basis. It is a more precise method than the moving average approach, but suffers from two major disadvantages. The first, which is a disadvantage of all time series methods, is that we are extrapolating into the future and, as we discussed in Chapter 7, extrapolation always carries some risk. The second, which is particular to regression, is its failure to respond to changes in trend. Unless we deliberately restrict ourselves to say only the past twelve months' data, then regression will always produce the best straight line through all the data. It needs little imagination to see the effect this would have on a forecast if a positive trend were to reverse. The moving average will always, eventually, follow a change in trend.

Exercise 54
Forecast demand for the first quarter of 1988 from the following data using regression to extract the trend. Compare your answer with that found in Exercise 52.

Quarter	1985	1986	1987
1	22	24	25
2	41	53	60
3	36	55	52
4	18	27	32

Regression may be used as a forecasting technique when we are able to propose a causal relationship between that which we are forecasting and some other known data. For this to be useful there has to be some lag, for instance admissions to hospital with bronchitis may be related to low temperature and high humidity. If it takes a week for the condition to develop, then we could forecast demand from the weather. Unfortunately, causal relationships are rarely that simple and we usually find that we are dealing with several causes, that the relationships are fairly poor, and that they are rarely linear. The statistical methods necessary to handle such situations are well beyond the scope of this book, and the outcomes of such analyses are frequently of little real value.

■ 11.4 SUMMARY

In this chapter we have looked at one of the most pressing problems facing any business activity, that of predicting the future. We have seen that where an adequate volume of quantitative data is available, a set of statistical techniques called time series analysis is available. We have looked at some of the simpler forms of trend analysis using moving and weighted averages and regression, and at the extraction of seasonality. We have briefly considered the general area of causal models.

The field of forecasting is large and we have barely touched the surface. Some very sophisticated statistical procedures are used; however, there is no reason to suppose that a more sophisticated procedure will produce a better result. There are only two criteria that are important in judging a forecasting method:

1 It should produce a forecast with an acceptably low error.
2 It should produce a forecast in time to be useful and at an acceptable cost.

If a method satisfies these criteria, its theoretical basis is quite irrelevant. It is important to remember that circumstances change and that forecasting methods should be continuously reviewed. The fact that a method has worked well in the past does not mean that it will continue to work well in the future.

■ 11.5 STUDY AND EXAM TIPS

Questions on forecasting are usually quite explicit, and specify whether or not you should use moving average, exponential smoothing or regression. They also usually specify whether or not seasonality is to be considered, so it is particularly important to:

1 Read the question carefully – producing answers which are not asked for gains no marks and costs valuable time.

2 In multipart questions, pay particular attention to time. Do not spend more than ten minutes on a part worth only one-third of the marks. Questions frequently have second and third parts depending on the first (e.g. calculate a trend then calculate seasonal factors). Since failing to complete the first part means you cannot go on to the second, you must be particularly sure that you know what you are doing before you start.

3 In calculating a moving average, think carefully about the period. If you are given figures for three or four years divided into quarters, or three or four weeks divided into days, it is likely that seasonality is present and you should choose a year (or a week). Otherwise three to six periods is probably reasonable.

4 Look at your answer critically in the light of the data given. A forecast of 100 when all the data lies between 40 and 60 is almost certainly wrong. If your answer looks unreasonable, try to find out why. If you cannot, at least say that you think it is wrong.

■ SELF ASSESSMENT QUESTIONS

Answer the following questions and then check your answers against those at the end of the book. If you get any wrong, re-read the relevant parts of the chapter. If this does not help, then talk to your tutor about the problem.

1 A three-month moving average is:
(a) An average whose value changes every three months
(b) An average that is recalculated every three months
(c) An average of the past three months' data that is calculated every month
2 The sensitivity of a forecast is:
(a) Inversely proportional to the number of periods in the average
(b) Proportional to the number of periods in the average
(c) Inversely proportional to α
3 An insensitive forecast would be used when:
(a) There is no clear trend
(b) There is an obvious trend
(c) There is a lot of random variation
(d) Never

■ EXAMINATION QUESTIONS

The table shows the number of jobs completed by a double glazing contractor in each of the four-month periods shown for the years 1982–6.

Period	1982	1983	1984	1985	1986
January–April	124	135	149	154	171
May–August	367	378	390	402	416
September–December	225	237	246	259	273

(a) By means of a moving average find the trend and seasonal variation. (12 marks)
(b) Plot the original series and trend on the same graph and thereby estimate the trend value for the first quarter of 1988. (8 marks)

(Institute of Marketing 1988)

The table shows a company's exports in £thousands for each month of 1985 and 1986. Construct a Z chart for 1986 and explain how it is to be interpreted.

Month	Monthly exports in £000 1985	1986
Jan	25	31
Feb	46	52
Mar	52	55
Apr	64	71
May	81	83
Jun	87	92
Jul	93	104
Aug	104	112
Sep	76	103
Oct	62	71
Nov	34	50
Dec	21	36

(Institute of Marketing 1987)

A company's stocks of raw materials, between 1983 and 1987, were as follows:

Year	Quarter	Stocks (000 tons)
1983	1	154
	2	320
	3	448
	4	730
1984	1	140
	2	276
	3	335
	4	606
1985	1	118
	2	215
	3	305
	4	659
1986	1	150
	2	445
	3	476
	4	750

(a) By means of a moving average find the trend and the average seasonal effect for each quarter. (14 marks)

(b) Find the deseasonalised series from the first quarter of 1983 to the last quarter of 1986. (6 marks)

(Association of Buisness Executives 1987)

A city has undertaken a census of the numbers of people using its rapid transit rail system at various times of the day during a typical working week. The results of the census are summarised in the following table:

Day	Time of day				
	6 am–10 am	10 am–1 pm	1 pm–4 pm	4 pm–7 pm	7 pm–11 pm
Monday	308	205	301	420	220
Tuesday	387	198	292	408	240
Wednesday	350	180	284	414	251
Thursday	371	189	252	424	223
Friday	385	210	290	460	396

(a) Calculate the average seasonal variations for the various periods of the day; and

(b) Estimate how many people might be using the system during each period of the day if the daily total of people using the system is expected to rise to 2 million.

(*Association of Business Executives 1982*)

12 Statistical quality control

■ 12.1 INTRODUCTION

One of the most appropriate uses of statistical methods, and in particular sampling theory, is in the field of quality control. We have already looked at potential applications in Chapter 8, where we considered the use of samples to check on whether or not a particular manufacturing process was producing goods within specification. Statistical methods are extensively used to check on the quality of manufactured goods by the producer, and to check on the quality of received goods by the customer. Similar techniques are frequently used in non-manufacturing areas to check on the quality of paperwork, data or files.

In section 12.2 we will look at the application of statistical techniques to quality control in manufacturing and supply. In section 12.3 we will consider the application of statistical techniques to process control, an approach which many people consider superior since it seeks to prevent defects occurring, rather than merely detecting them after they have arisen. Since statistical approaches to quality management do not exist in isolation, we will briefly consider some of the other aspects in section 12.4.

■ 12.2 STATISTICAL QUALITY CONTROL

Statistical quality control is based upon a fundamental assumption that perfect quality is probably unattainable and certainly too expensive to be worth seeking. This is, at least in theory, true. We have already seen that no matter how well set up a manufacturing process is, and no matter how tight its tolerance is, the actual product property (e.g. weight, thickness etc.) we are concerned with will follow the normal distribution. Since the normal distribution is open-ended, any value is theoretically possible. Equally, 100 per cent inspection does not guarantee zero defects. The inspection process itself is prone to failure.

Let us consider a process that produces 5 per cent defectives, followed by an inspection process with a 5 per cent failure rate. This means that 5 per cent of the defectives are not detected at inspection so 5 per cent of 5 per cent ($0.05 \times 0.05 \times 100$) or 0.25 per cent defectives go on to the next stage. Even if we introduce a second inspection, we will still have 5 per cent of 0.25 per cent or 0.0125 per cent defectives. This is roughly 1 in 10 000, which may be considered small, but it is certainly not zero.

Statistical quality control accepts these limitations and seeks to ensure, in the most cost-effective way possible, that a predetermined level of defectives is not exceeded.

Statistical quality control is almost exclusively concerned with defects. We are not generally concerned about the cause or nature of the defect, merely with its presence. If you are testing a batch of bolts for acceptability, you are not concerned with whether they are oversize or undersize, but only whether they are outside specification. Since the issue is whether or not a component is defective, we are dealing with the binomial distribution. Fortunately we are almost always dealing with large values of n (the sample size) and small values of p (the probability of a defective) so we can simplify the process by using the Poisson approximation to the binomial distribution.

When we sample a batch, generally at a late stage in the process, or, if we are the customer, on receipt, we are faced with a number of possible actions:

1 Accept the batch
2 Take a further sample
3 Reject the batch

If we reject the batch we may then:

1 100 per cent inspect and scrap the defectives
2 100 per cent inspect and either reclassify or rework the defectives
3 Rework the batch
4 Reclassify the batch to a lower-quality specification.

Of course, if we are the customer in receipt of a defective batch, we would not rework the batch and we would expect financial compensation from the supplier for any of the other alternatives.

As with any sampling scheme, we have the type I error, which is the risk that we wrongly reject an acceptable batch, and the type II error, which is the risk that we wrongly accept a sub-standard batch. The type I error is usually referred to as the **producer's risk** and the type II error as the **consumer's risk**.

The key measure of the effectiveness of a sampling scheme is its **operating characteristic**. This is a measure of its ability to discriminate between acceptable and defective batches. It is usually represented as a graph of percentage of batches accepted against percentage defectives in the batch. Figure 57 shows an ideal operating characteristic for a situation where up to 5 per cent defectives are acceptable. Such a characteristic is, of course, unattainable in practice.

12.2.1 Single sampling schemes

The simplest sampling scheme is one where we take a single sample of size n from each batch of size N. The batch is accepted if the number of defectives in the sample does not exceed the **acceptance number**, c. Such schemes are sometimes referred to as N, n, c schemes.

Let us consider a situation where N, the batch size, is 1000, and the percentage

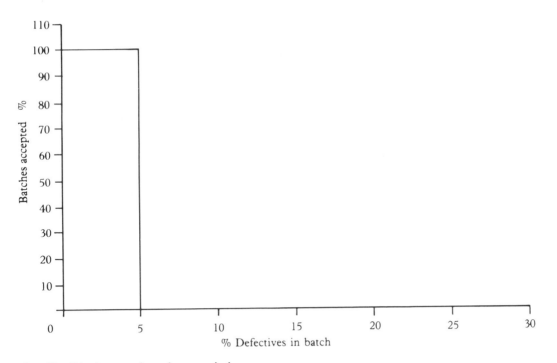

Fig. 57   Ideal operating characteristic

of defectives acceptable (the **acceptable quality level**, usually called the **AQL**) is 5 per cent.

If we take a scheme where the sample size n is 50, and the maximum permitted defectives c is 2, we can plot the operating characteristic by calculating the probability of >2 defectives in 50 for various percentage defectives in the batch. The probability of n defectives is $a^n e^{-a}/n!$. This is shown in Table 55.

If we increase the sample size and the allowed defectives, we get the situation shown in Table 56.

Figure 58 shows the operating characteristics.

It is obvious from Tables 55 and 56 and Fig. 58 that neither scheme is especially good, but that the larger sample size gives a more discriminating characteristic.

Table 55   1000, 50, 2 scheme

Actual % *defectives*	*Mean* *(np)*	*P(0)*	*P(1)*	*P(2)*	*Proportion* *accepted*
0.00	0.00	1.00	0.00	0.00	1.00
1.00	0.50	0.61	0.30	0.08	0.99
2.50	1.25	0.29	0.36	0.22	0.87
5.00	2.50	0.08	0.21	0.26	0.54
7.50	3.75	0.02	0.09	0.17	0.28
10.00	5.00	0.01	0.03	0.08	0.12
20.00	10.00	0.00	0.00	0.00	0.00

Table 56   1000, 100, 4 scheme

Actual % defectives	Mean (np)	P(0)	P(1)	P(2)	P(3)	P(4)	Proportion accepted
0.00	0.00	1.00	0.00	0.00	0.00	0.00	1.00
1.00	1.00	0.37	0.37	0.18	0.06	0.02	1.00
2.50	2.50	0.08	0.21	0.26	0.21	0.13	0.89
5.00	5.00	0.01	0.03	0.08	0.14	0.18	0.44
7.50	7.50	0.00	0.00	0.02	0.04	0.07	0.13
10.00	10.00	0.00	0.00	0.00	0.01	0.02	0.03
20.00	20.00	0.00	0.00	0.00	0.00	0.00	0.00

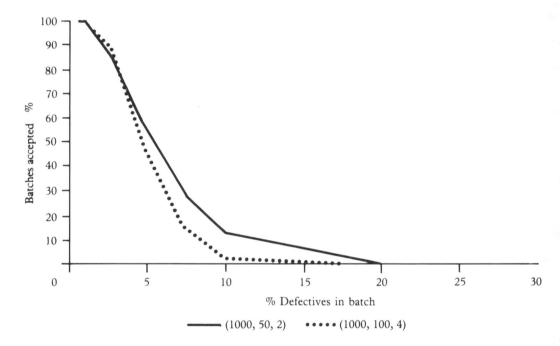

Fig. 58   Operating characteristics of single sample schemes

Even this allows 13 per cent of batches with 7.5 per cent defects through, while rejecting 11 per cent of batches with only 2.5 per cent defectives.

Exercise 55
Plot the operating characteristic for N = 1000, n = 100, c = 0. Compare this with the characteristic for 1000, 100, 4.

We cannot calculate the consumer's and producer's risks without specifying the actual percentage defectives we expect to see. This is usually referred to as the **process average percentage defective** or **PAPD**. Actual batches will have percentage defectives which vary about this figure. In fact, about 50 per cent of batches will exceed this, so the customer must be prepared to accept a higher figure than the PAPD in individual batches (if he will not, then we must seek to reduce the PAPD, or accept 100 per cent inspection). The maximum percentage defects the customer is prepared to accept in an individual batch is called the **lot tolerance percentage defectives** or **LTPD**.

It may be that the customer is prepared to accept an average percentage defectives greater than the PAPD. The average percentage defectives that the customer is prepared to accept is known as the **acceptable quality level** or **AQL**. It is often assumed to be the same as the PAPD.

Figure 59 shows an operating characteristic with an AQL of 1.5 per cent and an LTPD of 4 per cent. The producer's risk is the probability of rejecting batches with less than 1.5 per cent defectives while the consumer's risk is the probability of accepting batches with more than 4 per cent defectives.

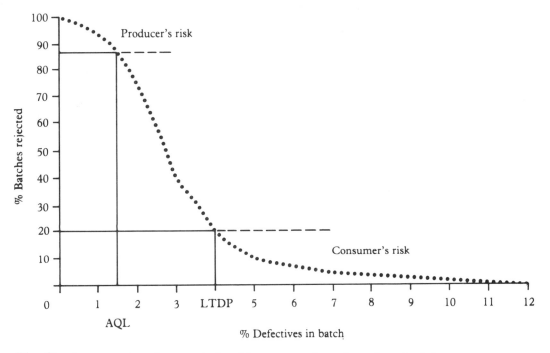

Fig. 59 An operating characteristic with consumer's and producer's risks

Generally, the choice of scheme is based upon balancing the cost of sampling plus the cost of reprocessing rejected good batches, against the cost of accepting batches which should be rejected. The cost of sampling and processing is usually easily determined. The cost of the consumer's risk is more difficult to specify and there are several alternatives:

1 If we are inspecting a batch prior to passing it to the next stage of the process, then we can no doubt specify the consequences of trying to further process an unacceptable batch.

2 If we are sampling prior to supplying a customer, then we are concerned with the probability that the customer's acceptance sampling will pick up the defective batch and the effect that will have on future trade with that customer as well as the cost of making restitution.

3 If we are the customer setting up an acceptance scheme, then we are in a similar position to 1.

The setting of risks is usually a matter of judgement. The specification of the sampling scheme once these have been specified, and when the AQL and LTPD are known, is usually a matter of looking up the required N, n and c in published tables.

Where rejection of a batch results in 100 per cent inspection, the sampling scheme may be based upon the **average outgoing quality level** or **AOQL** rather than the AQL. It is an interesting characteristic of acceptance sampling schemes with 100 per cent inspection of rejected batches that as average quality declines, the AOQL rises and then falls again. Initially, with perfect batches there will be no defectives. A small number of defectives will not generally be picked up by the scheme, but as the number rises, more and more batches will be 100 per cent inspected and the residues of those batches will be almost completely defect-free. The AOQL will thus rise to a maximum and then as more and more batches are 100 per cent inspected, it will begin to fall again. This effect is shown in Fig. 60. It is an important benefit of acceptance sampling that a maximum AOQL can be specified which is quite independent of the PAPD.

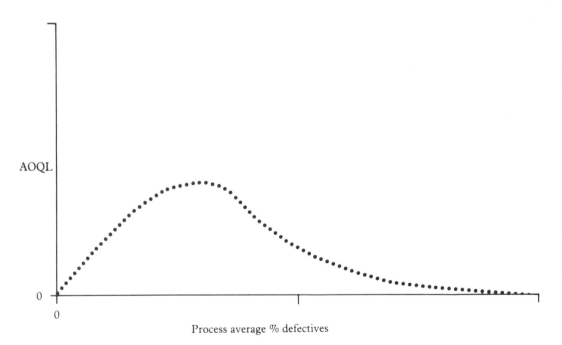

Fig. 60   Average outgoing quality

12.2.2   Multistage sampling

The rationale behind multistage sampling is the same as that behind rejecting hypotheses at the 1 per cent level and accepting them if they could not be rejected at the 5 per cent level, which we considered in Chapter 9.

If a small sample gives a clear indication that a batch is acceptable or, conversely, that it is defective, then the batch is either accepted or rejected. If the sample is inconclusive, then a further sample is taken. The combined larger sample will be more discriminating, and should give a clear indication of acceptability. The principle is illustrated in Table 57.

Table 57   A two-stage sampling process

1.   Inspect 50
2.   If defects <2, accept
3.   If defects >5, reject
4.   If defects = 3 or defects = 4, then inspect a further 50
and:
5.   If total defects <7, accept
6.   If total defects ≥7, reject

While such schemes offer a good compromise between cost and discrimination, their greater complexity makes them more difficult to operate correctly, and many organisations prefer to use the simpler single-stage sample.

Another alternative is the continuous sampling scheme. Here sampling, after a certain minimum is reached, continues until a clear decision is reached. This is illustrated in Fig. 61.

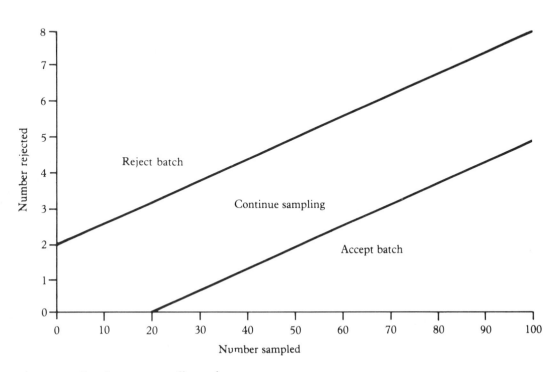

Fig. 61   Continuous sampling scheme

■ 12.3 STATISTICAL PROCESS CONTROL

The objective of statistical process control is to ensure that the process continues to produce to specification. There is an implicit assumption that the process is capable of producing to specification. If we are trying to produce metal rods with a diameter of 20 mm ± 0.2 mm on a machine which produces to a tolerance of ±0.3 mm, then we must accept 100 per cent inspection since neither statistical process control nor statistical quality control will be of any help. The first requirement is that the process tolerance (the precision with which the process can produce) must be tighter than the product tolerance (the precision required by the customer). The size of the difference between these will directly affect the difficulty of the task of process control and the size of sample required to carry it out.

12.3.1 Control of attributes

As we know, it is much easier to measure attributes than values. Much process control measurement is based upon simple gauges which classify the controlled dimension (thickness, weight, electrical resistance, viscosity etc.) as acceptable or unacceptable. The statistical procedures are very similar to those described in section 12.2, and rejection of a sample may well lead to 100 per cent inspection of the production from which the sample came, but the main objective of process control sampling is to determine whether or not the process is operating correctly, and the main action in case of rejection is to reset the process. Sampling is therefore usually carried out intermittently at regular intervals rather than on a batch basis.

The most convenient way of representing the results of the inspection process and indicating the requirement for action is the **control chart**.

First we establish the tolerance within which we expect the process to operate. For example, if a process can produce metal rods to a tolerance of ±0.2 mm, and we have a requirement to produce to a specification of 20 mm ± 0.4 mm, then we might accept a variation in the machine setting of ±0.1 mm. The objective of process control sampling is to establish when the process has drifted outside this range.

If we construct a simple gauge which does not allow oversize products to enter, but allows undersize products to pass right through (a **go no-go** gauge) then we can still sample by attribute. We would set the sample size and the gauge size such that a correctly set process would produce say 10 per cent rejects. (Note: these are rejects in terms of our internally set control limits, not rejects to the product specification.) If we take a sample of ten, we know that the mean defectives is:

$$np = 10 \times 0.1 = 1$$

and the standard deviation is:

$$\sqrt{np(1 - p)} = \sqrt{10 \times 0.1 \times 0.9} = 0.95$$

We would now usually set two limits, a warning limit at $+2\sigma$, and an action limit at $+3\sigma$. These are:

Warning limit = $1 + 2 \times 0.95 = 2.9$
Action limit   = $1 + 3 \times 0.95 = 3.85$

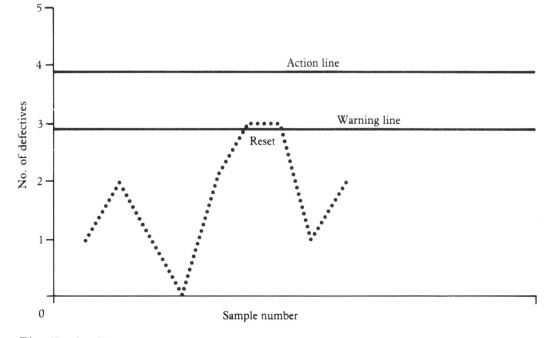

Fig. 62   Attribute control chart

The procedure is now to take samples of ten at regular intervals during the running of the process, to count the number of defectives in the sample and to record this on the control chart illustrated in Fig. 62. If a sample exceeds the action limit, the process is stopped and adjusted. If a sample exceeds the warning limit, a second sample is taken immediately and if this also exceeds the warning limit the process is again stopped for adjustment. We are again following the principle that there is an area of indecision between two levels of significance. Since this is a one-tailed test, the levels are actually 2.3 per cent (the warning limit) and 0.13 per cent (the action limit).

Occasionally, attribute control charts include lower warning and action limits as well. This may seem surprising since producing fewer defectives than expected is hardly a problem, but it may indicate an improvement in the process which warrants investigation, or it may indicate a failure of the measuring process.

Exercise 56
Calculate the upper and lower action and warning limits for a sample size of twenty and an average defective of 15 per cent.

12.3.2   Control of dimensions

Control by actual measurement is much more powerful and discriminating, but also much more expensive. It takes far more skill and time to measure the diameter of ten pieces of metal rod with a micrometer than it does to feed them into a go no-go gauge. In addition, the sample mean must be calculated. Unlike attribute sampling, this is not a task that can usually be left to the machine operator, and a separate inspector is usually employed. The cost of sampling by measurement is often as much as twenty times greater than sampling by attribute. For this reason it is much less frequently used.

When it is used for routine process control, the principle is exactly the same as for attribute sampling. Control charts with warning limits at $\pm 2\sigma$ and action limits at $\pm 3\sigma$ are created. The only difference is that it is actual dimension which is plotted, and the sampler has to calculate the sample mean.

■ 12.4 OTHER APPROACHES TO QUALITY MANAGEMENT

As we have seen above, quality control is expensive in terms of inspection costs and, where necessary, recovery costs. Failure is also expensive: defective or out-of-range components and materials can give rise to costs out of all proportion to the value of the component, as in such things as the failure of a valve on an oil rig, or a tail rotor on a helicopter.

Defective components can also damage production plant which, on a production line, carries the added penalty of the cost of production lost while the fault is repaired.

Statistical quality control, properly operated, guarantees a maximum level of defects. It cannot guarantee zero defects. It carries other hidden costs. A batch must be held in stock while awaiting acceptance testing. Sometimes testing is done at the suppliers prior to shipment, but we still have delay and stockholding costs, wherever they are incurred. Batches must be relatively large to make the sampling process cost-effective.

Recently there has been a reaction against this traditional view. Pressure to reduce costs and increase responsiveness has caused manufacturing firms to reduce stocks and move towards arranging frequent small consignment deliveries. This is sometimes known as the **just in time** approach. The result of this is that we can no longer wait for orthodox acceptance testing to run its course. Consignments are used as soon as delivered and defects cannot be tolerated. The approach of **total quality control** is to insist on the aim of zero defects at all stages. The customer monitors the supplier's production capability rather than the product. Statistical process control is stressed, together with a concentration on reducing manufacturing tolerances so that there is even less risk of exceeding product tolerances. Involvement of all personnel in issues of quality through the setting up of **quality circles**, whose role is to address any design, material, or process issues which have a bearing on quality, can have a dramatic effect. Partly this is through the development of an attitude of seeking to improve quality rather than seeking to contain defects. Equally, the breaking down of the barrier which often exists between the operator, who sees quality as someone else's problem, and the inspector, who is sometimes seen as being on the side of the customer and therefore an adversary of manufacturing, can lead to substantial improvement very quickly.

If statistical quality control is based upon the principle that perfect quality is not attainable and that a certain level of defects is in fact more cost-effective, the total quality concept is based upon the premiss that quality is everybody's problem and should be subject to continuous improvement. The two approaches are not necessarily mutually exclusive, and the balance between them must depend on the needs of the market and the production technology used.

12.5   SUMMARY

In this chapter we have looked, briefly, at one of the most common and important applications of statistical methods, the control of quality. We have looked in some detail at the application of sampling theory and the binomial distribution to acceptance testing by attribute, and then considered the application of the same methods to the monitoring of manufacturing processes. We have seen how control charts may be constructed to facilitate this process, and how the method can be further developed to cover measurement as well as attribute. Finally, we have considered the place of statistical methods in the overall context of quality management.

12.6   STUDY AND EXAM TIPS

Examination questions in this area have been rare in the past but the following points should be borne in mind:

1 Statistical quality control is only an extension of statistical inference covered in Chapter 9. Most of the comments in Chapter 9 therefore apply.

2 Is the question about attributes or a continuous variable? If about attributes, we are using the binomial distribution (or the Poisson approximation); if a continuous variable, then we are concerned with the normal distribution.

3 If you are discussing ideas such as AOQL, PAPD etc., define them clearly. It is all too easy to get initials mixed up, and if you have not defined the terms the examiner may well wonder if you know what you are talking about.

■ SELF ASSESSMENT QUESTIONS

Answer the following questions and then check your answers against those at the end of the book. If you get any wrong, re-read the relevant parts of the chapter. If this does not help, then talk to your tutor about the problem.

1 Define the following:
(a) AOQL
(b) PAPD
(c) AQL
(d) LTPD

2 The consumer's risk is:
(a) The risk that a consumer will find that the batch is defective
(b) The risk that an acceptable batch will be rejected
(c) The risk that a defective batch will be accepted

3 The producer's risk is:
(a) The risk that a consumer will find that the batch is defective
(b) The risk that an acceptable batch will be rejected
(c) The risk that a defective batch will be accepted

4 Exceeding the upper warning limit usually means:
(a) Stop the machine
(b) Reject the batch
(c) Take another sample

■ EXAMINATION QUESTIONS

A machine in a factory is designed to produce steel rods with a mean length of 20 cm and a standard deviation of 0.4 cm. Every hour a sample of sixteen rods is chosen and their mean length is calculated. On a particular Tuesday, the following results were obtained:

Time	Mean length	Time	Mean length
8.30 am	19.81	12.30 pm	19.95
9.30 am	20.20	2.30 pm	20.28
10.30 am	20.15	3.30 pm	20.36
11.30 am	19.70	4.30 pm	20.38

(a) Design a decision rule to decide at a 99.73 per cent level of confidence whether the machine is performing according to specification or not. (7 marks)
(NB: $z = 3$ at a 99.73 per cent level of confidence)

(b) Plot the results for the Tuesday samples on a chart and interpret the result. (13 marks)

(Association of Business Executives 1983)

Appendix 1   Answers to self assessment questions

■ CHAPTER 1

1   (a)
2   (b)
3   (b) and (e)
4   (b)
5   (b)

■ CHAPTER 2

1   (b)
2   (a) Mean
2   (b) Mean
2   (c) Median
2   (d) Mode
2   (e) Mean
2   (f) Mean
3   15 (there are three of them)
4   (b)

■ CHAPTER 3

1   9 to 24
2   (c)
3   (d)
4   (b) and (d)
5   (c)

■ CHAPTER 4

1 (a)
2 (c)
3 (d)
4 (c)

■ CHAPTER 5

1 (a) Binomial
1 (b) Poisson
1 (c) Non-standard
1 (d) Normal
1 (e) Non-standard
1 (f) Binomial
1 (g) Poisson
2 (a) and (b)
3 (b), (d) and (e)
4 (d)

■ CHAPTER 6

1 (b)
2 (c)
3 (a)
4 (a)
5 (b)
6 (b)
7 (b)

■ CHAPTER 7

1 (a)
2 (b)
3 (b)

■ CHAPTER 8

1 (b), (c) (and (d) if the firm were very large)
2 (d)
3 (b)
4 (c)
5 (b)

■ CHAPTER 9

1   (a) t
1   (b) t
1   (c) z
1   (d) t
1   (e) F
1   (f) χ^2
2   (d)

■ CHAPTER 10

1   (a)
2   (b)
3   (a)
4   (a)

■ CHAPTER 11

1   (c)
2   (a) and (c)
3   (a) and (c)

■ CHAPTER 12

1   (a) Average outgoing quality level = the average number of defectives after inspection
1   (b) Process average percentage defectives = the average number of defectives in batches arriving at inspection
1   (c) Acceptable quality level = the average percentage defectives acceptable to the customer
1   (d) Lot tolerance percentage defectives = the maximum percentage defectives acceptable in any one batch
2   (c)
3   (b)
4   (c)

Appendix 2   Answers to exercises

■ CHAPTER 1   PRESENTING STATISTICS

Exercise 1   Reorganise data into four and sixteen groups

The total range we are dealing with is 8.0 to 15.0 (to the nearest whole number), giving us a range of 7 (15 − 8). This is not easy to divide into either four or sixteen groups, and we really need to expand the range to 8 to make this convenient. A range of 7.5 to 15.5 does this, giving a group size of 2.0 for four groups and 0.5 for sixteen groups. Dealing with four groups first, our first group starts at 7.5 and has a size of 2.0 ((15.5 − 7.5)/4), so it ends at 9.5. We must not forget that we really mean <9.5 here and to eliminate ambiguity we would say 7.5–9.4. The bottom of the second group is, of course, the top of the first group less the < sign, 9.5, and its top is 9.5 + 2.0 = 11.5 but, as before, we would write 11.4. Following the same procedure, the other groups become:

> 11.5–13.4
> 13.5–15.4

When data is sorted, it is a simple task to count the number of values in each group, and we find that there are twelve in the first group, thirty-two in the second, thirty-six in the third and twenty in the last. In tabular form, we have:

7.5– 9.4	12
9.5–11.4	32
11.5–13.4	36
13.5–15.5	20

Always check the total to make sure you have counted everything once, and nothing twice. It is 100 here.

When data is not sorted, make a table with a row for each group, then work through the data putting a tick against the group to which each value in turn belongs. When you have finished, count the ticks against each group.

With sixteen groups, we proceed in exactly the same way, specifying the groups as 7.5–7.9, 8.0–8.4 etc. and counting the values in each group. The result is:

7.5– 7.9	0	11.5–11.9	6
8.0– 8.4	0	12.0–12.4	9
8.5– 8.9	2	12.5–12.9	11
9.0– 9.4	10	13.0–13.4	10
9.5– 9.9	9	13.5–13.9	9
10.0–10.4	7	14.0–14.4	7
10.5–10.9	4	14.5–14.9	4
11.0–11.4	12	15.0–15.4	0

Again we check that the total is 100.

Which is best? Four groups gives us a very clear picture of the bulk lying between 9.5 and 13.5, but not much else. It even disguises the range by suggesting that some values may be as low as 7.5 or as high as 11.5. It is not a very satisfactory presentation – too much information has been lost and it illustrates the need to arrange the grouping to suit the data rather than vice versa. Sixteen groups gives a very clear picture of the distribution of values, but it could be argued that it gives too much detail, and that the picture given by seven groups is even clearer.

Exercise 2   Plot histograms for the above

The key to a good graph is the correct choice of scale for the axes. With four groups we have a maximum number in any one group of thirty-six, so the y axis could be 0 to 40 or 0 to 50; 0 to 100 might seem reasonable, but it would leave more than half the graph empty. It is now a simple matter to plot and label the axes and draw the histogram as in Fig. 63.

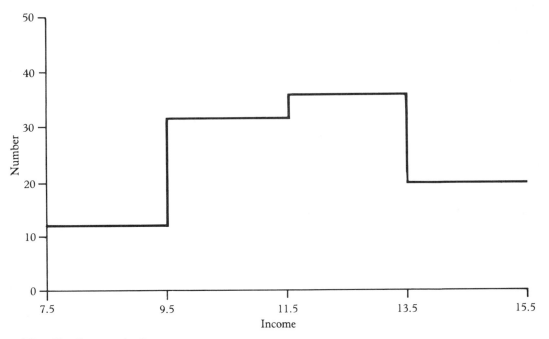

Fig. 63   Income in four groups

With sixteen groups, we need to redraw the x axis to allow for the new groups, and we need to redraw the y axis to allow for the new maximum of twelve. A y axis of 0 to 15 or 0 to 20 is suitable (Fig. 64).

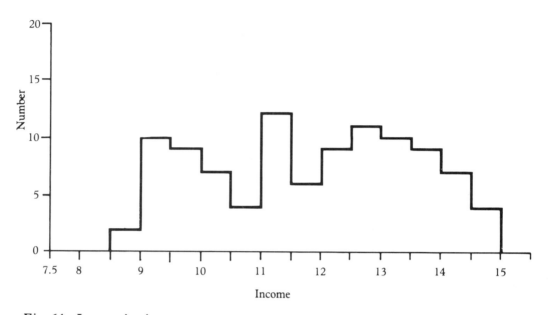

Fig. 64 Income in sixteen groups

Always use graph paper and a ruler when drawing graphs by hand, and always use the whole sheet, allowing adequate margins. Appearance is important.

Exercise 3   Draw ogives for the above

We can present both ogives on one graph, since the axes will be identical.
  First we need to tabulate running totals as follows:

Group	Cumulative total (16)	Cumulative total (4)
7.5– 7.9	0	
8.0– 8.4	0	
8.5– 8.9	2	
9.0– 9.4	12	12
9.5– 9.9	21	
10.0–10.4	28	
10.5–10.9	32	
11.0–11.4	44	44
11.5–11.9	50	
12.0–12.4	59	

12.5–12.9	70	
13.0–13.4	80	80
13.5–13.9	89	
14.0–14.4	96	
14.5–14.9	100	
15.0–15.4	100	100

Our x axis is obviously going to be 0 to 100. The choice of y axis is less obvious. Should we use 7.5 to 15.5, or something less spuriously precise like 5 to 20 or even 0 to 20? There is no right answer. People tend to expect round figures like 0 to 5 or 10 on axes, but we will be making better use of the paper if we use a more precise scale. Two examples are given, you must make up your own mind as to which is best (Figs. 65 and 66).

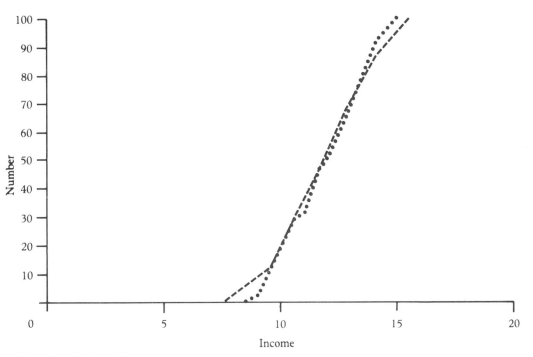

Fig. 65 Ogive of incomes

Once we have chosen our axes we simply plot the points and join them. Some people try to join the points with a smooth curve, rather than with straight lines. This is probably more realistic, but the straight-line approach is easier and does not disguise the fact that we do not know the shape of the curve between the points.

Exercise 4 Bar chart of total sales by product

We know the total sales by product since this is given in Table 5. The only decisions are whether it should be a horizontal or vertical chart, and the scale of the y axis. Since the maximum sales are 486, a scale of 0 to 500 will be suitable. A vertical bar chart is shown (Fig. 67).

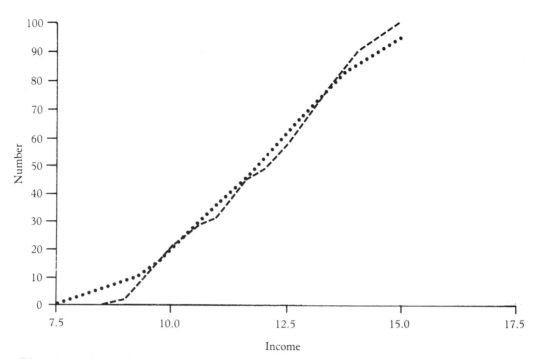

Fig. 66 **Ogive of incomes**

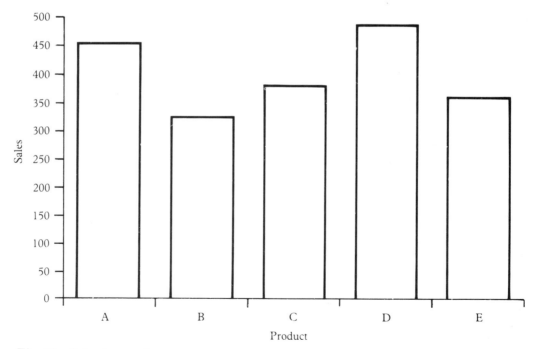

Fig. 67 **Sales by product**

Exercise 5   Stacked bar chart by region

The y axis is again defined by the maximum sales (by region this time), which is 661. This is an awkward number, and scales of 0 to 700, 750 or 1000 might be used. Having drawn the axes and chosen a scale, we first draw the bars for product A. We then draw, on top of these, the bars for product B so that the tops of the bars come up to the total of sales for A and B. We then add C to this and so on until we have plotted all products (Fig. 68).

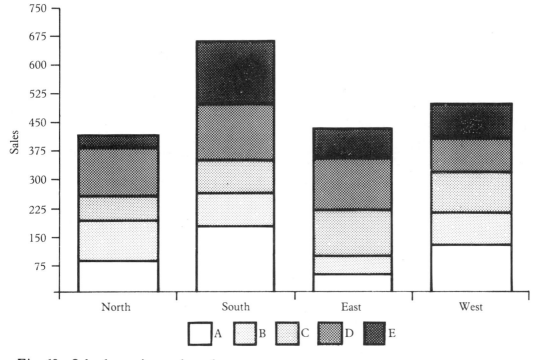

Fig. 68   Sales by region and product

Exercise 6   Cartesian graph of profit against sales

In this exercise we are only interested in profit and sales, not the year. Since profit depends on sales rather than sales on profit, profit will be our y axis and sales the x axis. The y axis scale should probably start at 0 and go to either 7 or 10. The x axis scale could start at 10 or even 15, but is probably better started at 0, rising to 60, 75 or 100.

Choose your scales, draw the axes and then plot the eight points.

There are a number of options now open. We could just leave the points, join them with straight lines (as Fig. 69), try to join them with a smooth curve, or try to draw a straight line as near as possible to all the points. Unless we have reason to believe that the data is following some mathematical rule which justifies a curve or a straight line (see Chapter 7), the first two options are the safest since they make no assumptions.

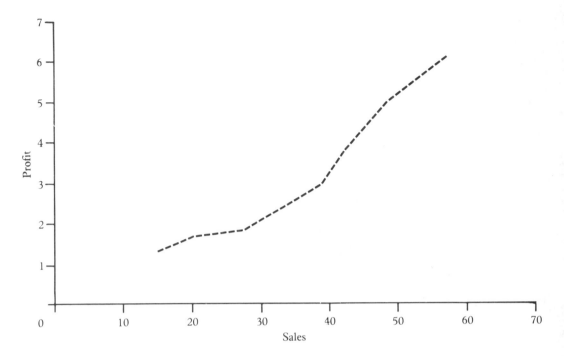

Fig. 69 Profit and sales

■ CHAPTER 2   WHAT IS AN AVERAGE?

Exercise 7   Uses of the average

The potential list is almost endless, but among the most common are situations where we wish to work out a total of some sort from something which varies, for instance the time of a journey from the average speed of a car. The average is also frequently used to monitor quality (people tend to judge the quality of the weather by the average temperature, or rainfall, or hours of sunshine), and is the basis behind many indices (cost of living, share indices etc.). We will look at indices in Chapter 10.

Exercise 8   Arithmetic mean of 100 incomes

The sum of the values is 1 178.04 and, since there are 100 values, the mean is 11.7804.

Exercise 9   Mean defectives per worker

Our first task is to calculate the mid-point of each group. Since we are dealing with integers here, the task is fairly easy. The first group actually does go from 0 to 2, not to 2.5 or 2.9, or any other intermediate value, so the mid-point is quite simply halfway between 0 and 2, i.e. 1. The same procedure gives us the other mid-points as shown. We now multiply the mid-points by the number of occurrences in each group, as shown. If we sum this product we get the total number of defectives, and dividing this by the number of workers gives us the mean number of defectives per worker.

Defects	Number	Mid-point	Number × mid-point
0– 2	5	1	5
3– 5	7	4	28
6– 8	6	7	42
9–11	5	10	50
12–14	4	13	52
15–17	10	16	160
18–20	11	19	209
21–23	9	22	198
24–26	6	25	150
27–29	4	28	112
Sum	67		1006
Mean =	1006/67 =		15.01

Exercise 10   Use of mean family size

The population of a town of 40 000 families is 40 000 times the mean family size of 3.78:

$$40\,000 \times 3.78 = 151\,200$$

Assuming that each dwelling accommodates one family, then the number of dwellings required equals the number of families: 120 000 people represent 120 000/3.78 = 31 746.031 families and, therefore, 31 746 dwellings (obviously we must ignore the 0.031).

Exercise 11   The median defects per worker

The data is already ranked, so we calculate the cumulative total of workers as shown:

Defects	Number	Cumulative total
0– 2	5	5
3– 5	7	12
6– 8	6	18
9–11	5	23
12–14	4	27
15–17	10	37
18–20	11	48
21–23	9	57
24–26	6	63
27–29	4	67

There are 67 workers, so the mid-point corresponds to number 34. The 34th lies in the group 15 to 17 defects. There are 10 workers in this group and the median lies at number 6 so, by proportion, it will lie 6/10ths of the way between 15 and 17, or at $15 + 2 \times 6/10$. However, since we are dealing with integer values here, the median value must be 16.

Exercise 12   Geometric mean share price

The product of the six values is 609 405 350 400 and the sixth root is 92.08. Your calculator probably will not manage this level of accuracy and may not even be able to multiply the six numbers. If you have this problem, then convert the share prices into pounds by dividing by 100 first.

■ CHAPTER 3   MEASURES OF DISPERSION

Exercise 13   Mean absolute deviation

First we need to find the mean, which is 12.18. We then subtract this from each of our original values, but ignoring negative signs (i.e. all results are treated as positive). It is a simple matter now to sum the deviations and find their mean, which is 1.24.

Income	Absolute deviation	Income	Absolute deviation
12.00	0.17	9.00	3.17
13.20	1.03	9.90	2.27
13.50	1.33	12.50	0.33
12.30	0.13	12.20	0.03
12.40	0.23	12.10	0.07
13.10	0.93	14.50	2.33
13.20	1.03	9.10	3.07
11.50	0.67	10.20	1.97
13.80	1.63	11.20	0.97
13.20	1.03	13.90	1.73
12.50	0.33	11.80	0.37
11.60	0.57	14.70	2.53
14.50	2.33	13.90	1.73
11.80	0.37	9.10	3.07
11.40	0.77	11.10	1.07
Sum		365.20	37.26
Mean		12.17	1.24

Exercise 14   Standard deviation

We set up a table as shown, with the individual values and their squares. We then sum each column.

Income	Income squared	Income	Income squared
12.00	144.00	9.00	81.00
13.20	174.24	9.90	98.01
13.50	182.25	12.50	156.25
12.30	151.29	12.20	148.84
12.40	153.76	12.10	146.41
13.10	171.61	14.50	210.25
13.20	174.24	9.10	82.81
11.50	132.25	10.20	104.04
13.80	190.44	11.20	125.44
13.20	174.24	13.90	193.21
12.50	156.25	11.80	139.24
11.60	134.56	14.70	216.09
14.50	210.25	13.90	193.21
11.80	139.24	9.10	82.81
11.40	129.96	11.10	123.21
Sum		365.20	4519.40
Mean		12.17	150.65

We now calculate the mean and substitute it, the sum of squares and the number of observations into the equation

$$\sqrt{(\Sigma x^2/n - \bar{x}^2)}$$

and we get $\sqrt{(150.65 - 12.17^2)}$

$$= \sqrt{2.46} = 1.57$$

Exercise 15   Standard deviation with grouped data

This is an extension of the table developed in Exercise 9 (Chapter 2), and we use the same basic approach. First we identify the mid-point of each group, then we square the mid-point and multiply it by the number of occurrences in that group to find the sum of squares for the group. This is shown in the table. The sum of the final column is the total sum of squares.

Defects	Number	Mid-point (MP)	Number × MP	MP squared	Number × MP squared
0– 2	5	1	5	1	5
3– 5	7	4	28	16	112
6– 8	6	7	42	49	294
9–11	5	10	50	100	500
12–14	4	13	52	169	676
15–17	10	16	160	256	2 560
18–20	11	19	209	361	3 971
21–23	9	22	198	484	4 356
24–26	6	25	150	625	3 750
27–29	4	28	112	784	3 136
Sum	67		1006		19 360
Mean =	1006/67 =		15.01		

Substituting in the equation, we get

$$\sqrt{(19\ 360/67 - 15.01^2)}$$
or $\sqrt{(288.95522 - 225.3001)} = \sqrt{63.65512} = 7.978$

■ CHAPTER 4   PROBABILITY

Exercise 16   Probability of throwing six

A fair die is, by definition, a cube with 1, 2, 3, 4, 5 and 6 spots on its six faces. When thrown it will fall in such a way that all faces are equally likely to face upwards. Since one face must face upwards (probability of 1.0), the probability that any specified face will face upwards is 1/6 (the number of faces). Since the face with six spots is a specified face, the answer to the question is 1/6 or 0.1667.

Exercise 17   Tossing a drawing pin

This is an exercise in calculating an empirical probability in the absence of any theoretical basis.

The total number of observations is:

897 + 1342 = 2239

Of these, 897 were the outcome of interest, the pin landing point down, so the probability of the pin landing point down is:

897/2239 = 0.4006

Exercise 18   Drawing playing cards

(a) There are thirteen cards in each of the four suits, therefore the probability of drawing a card of any specified suit is:

13/52 = 0.25

Using the addition rule:

$P(\text{H or D}) = P(\text{H}) + P(\text{D}) = 0.25 + 0.25 = 0.5$

Alternatively, we could say that there are twenty-six hearts and diamonds, therefore the probability of drawing a heart or diamond is 26/52 = 0.5.

(b) There are four of each rank of card in a pack so the probability of drawing any particular rank is:

4/52 = 0.07692

Again the addition rule tells us:

$P(\text{J or Q or K or A}) = P(\text{J}) + P(\text{Q}) + P(\text{K}) + P(\text{A})$
$= 4 \times 0.07692 = 0.3077$

In both these cases the outcomes are mutually exclusive.

Exercise 19   Drawing playing cards (2)

(a) This can be expressed as:

$P(A$ and A and A and $A)$

which means that we are using the multiplication rule, so we have:

$P(4A) = P(A)^4$

We know that $P(A) = 0.07692$ so:

$P(4A) = 0.07692^4 = 0.00004$

(b) This can be expressed as:

$P(AC$ and $3D) = P(AC) \times P(D)^3$

We know that the probability of a diamond is 0.25, the probability of the ace of clubs is, of course, $1/52 = 0.01923$ since there is only one ace of clubs, so:

$P(AC$ and $3D) = 0.01932 \times 0.25^3 = 0.0003$

In both these cases the outcomes are independent.

Exercise 20   Venn diagram

Clubs represent 25 per cent of the total pack, and aces just over 7.5 per cent. One ace is a club. While clarity is more important than scale, it helps to keep things more or less in proportion and the result should look something like Fig. 70.

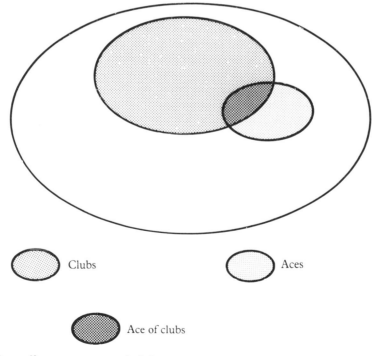

Fig. 70 Venn diagram, aces and clubs

Exercise 21   Probability tree

It does not matter whether we start with the coin or the die. If you start with the coin you will have two branches each followed by six. If you start with the die you will have six branches each followed by two. In either case you get the same twelve outcomes (Fig. 71).

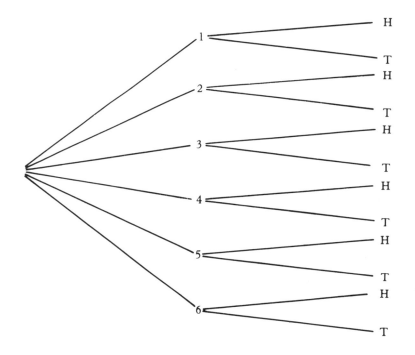

Fig. 71   Probability tree, die and coin

Exercise 22   Arranging five beads

This is a permutation of five from eight:

$$^8P_5 = 8!/(8 - 5)! = 8!/3!$$
$$= 40\ 320 = 6\ 720$$

Exercise 23   Combinations

(a) $^6C_4 = 6!/(4!(6 - 4)!)$
   $= 720/(24 \times 2) = 15$

(b) $^7C_3 = 7!/(3!(7 - 3)!)$
   $= 5040/(6 \times 24) = 35$

Exercise 24   Coin tossing

(a) The probability of three tails and one head in any one way is $0.5^4 = 0.0625$. The number of ways of getting one head is:

$$^4C_1 = 4!/3! = 4$$

Therefore the probability of three tails and one head is:

$$4 \times 0.0625 = 0.25$$

(b) This is equivalent to:

$$P(4\text{HT or }5\text{H})$$
$$P(4\text{HT}) = {}^5C_4 \times 0.5^5$$
$$= 5!/4! \times 0.0015625$$
$$= 0.0078125$$
$$P(5\text{H}) = 0.5^5 = 0.0015625$$

so the answer is:

$$0.0078125 + 0.0015625 = 0.009375$$

■ CHAPTER 5   DISTRIBUTIONS

Exercise 25   Probability of more than two rejects

Since we are interested in $P(\leqslant 2)$ we need to calculate $P(0)$, $P(1)$ and $P(2)$.

$$p = 0.05,\ q = 0.95 \text{ and } n = 10$$
$$P(0) = 0.95^{10} = 0.5987$$
$$P(1) = {}^{10}C_1 \times 0.05 \times 0.95^9 = 10 \times 0.05 \times 0.6302 = 0.3151$$
$$P(2) = {}^{10}C_2 \times 0.05^2 \times 0.95^8 = 45 \times 0.0025 \times 0.6634 = 0.0746$$

and the total is:

$$P(\leqslant 2) = 0.9884$$

therefore the probability of >2 rejects in ten is:

$$P(>2) = 0.0116$$

Exercise 26   Mean and standard deviation

We know that the mean is np and the standard deviation is $\sqrt{npq}$.
$n = 10$, $p = 0.05$ and $q = 0.95$, therefore:

Mean $= 10 \times 0.05 = 0.5$
Standard deviation $= \sqrt{10 \times 0.05 \times 0.95} = \sqrt{0.475} = 0.6892$

Exercise 27   Probability of six customers

The mean rate of arrival is ten per hour, so the rate per half-hour is $10/2 = 5$. We have:

$$P(6) = e^{-5} \times 5^6/6! = 0.002479 \times 15\,625/720 = 0.0538$$

Exercise 28   Probability of more than five calls

The mean is one call per 2 minutes which is 5/2 = 2.5 calls per 5 minutes.

$$P(>5) = 1.0 - (P(0) + P(1) + P(2) + P(3) + P(4) + P(5))$$
$$P(0) = e^{-2.5} = 0.08208$$
$$P(1) = e^{-2.5} \times 2.5 = 0.2025$$
$$P(2) = e^{-2.5} \times 2.5^2/2 = 0.2565$$
$$P(3) = e^{-2.5} \times 2.5^3/6 = 0.21375$$
$$P(4) = e^{-2.5} \times 2.5^4/24 = 0.1336$$
$$P(5) = e^{-2.5} \times 2.5^5/120 = 0.0668$$

Note that a simple way to calculate these results is simply to multiply the previous answer by 2.5 and divide the result by the first term in the new factorial, i.e.

$$P(3) = P(2) \times 2.5/3$$

Adding these and subtracting from 1 we get:

$$P(>5) = 1 - 0.95523 = 0.04477$$

Exercise 29   Probability of underweight sugar bag

We know that:

Mean = 1.045
Standard deviation = 0.02

and we are interested in $P(<1.0)$, so z is given by

$$z = (1.045 - 1)/0.02 = 2.25$$

Looking up $z = 2.25$ in the tables, we get a probability of 0.01222. This is the area away from the mean and it is the area away from the mean that we are interested in, so the answer is 0.01222.

Exercise 30   Probability of being underweight of 2.5 per cent

2.5 per cent is a probability of 0.025. Again we are interested in the area away from the mean so we simply find the z which most nearly corresponds to 0.025, which is exactly 1.96. We therefore need to set our machine for a mean 1.96 standard deviations above 1 or:

$$1 + 1.96 \times 0.02 = 1.0392 \text{ (we would probably say 1.04)}$$

Exercise 31   Reject probability for process mean of 5.01 mm

We have:

Mean = 5.01
Standard deviation = 0.015
Limits 4.95 and 5.05

For $P(<4.95)$ we have:

$z = (5.01 - 4.95)/0.015 = 4.00$ and $P = 0.00003$

For $P(>5.05)$ we have:

$z = (5.05 - 5.01)/0.015 = 2.67$ and $P = 0.00379$

so the total probability is 0.00382.

Exercise 32   Probability of being 165 to 180 cm tall

We have:

Mean $= 173$
Standard deviation $= 8$
Limits 165 and 180

Your sketch will show you that the limits enclose the mean, so we are interested in the area between the mean and our z values. This means that we will have to subtract the probability figures from the table from 0.5 to get the probability of interest.

For $P(165$ to $173)$:

$z = (173 - 165)/8 = 1$ and $P = 0.5 - 0.15866 = 0.34134$

For $P(173$ to $180)$:

$z = (180 - 173)/8 = 0.875$ and $P = 0.5 - 0.191 = 0.309$

so the total probability is 0.65034.

Note that $z = 0.875$ does not appear in our tables, 0.191 is about halfway between the values for 0.87 and 0.88. It is actually 0.19079, but there is no point in being that precise since the normal distribution curve is not a straight line.

■ CHAPTER 6   CORRELATION

Exercise 33   Correlation coefficient of degrees Celsius v. degrees Fahrenheit

The figures in the first two columns were given in Table 27. We first calculate the figures in the next three columns (x^2, y^2 and xy). If you have any wrong, re-check your arithmetic.

Celsius	Fahrenheit			
Y	X	$Y \times Y$	$X \times X$	$X \times Y$
0	32	0	1 024	0
10	50	100	2 500	500
20	68	400	4 624	1 360
30	86	900	7 396	2 580
40	104	1 600	10 816	4 160
50	122	2 500	14 884	6 100
60	140	3 600	19 600	8 400
70	158	4 900	24 964	11 060

We then sum each column and get the following results:

	Y	X	Y × Y	X × X	Y × X
Sum	280	760	14 000	85 808	34 160

Now we calculate the mean of x and y:
  Mean of $x = 760/8 = 95.00$
  Mean of $y = 280/8 = 35.00$

and the standard deviation of x and y:

Standard deviation of $x = \sqrt{(85\ 808/8 - (760/8)^2)}$
$$= (10\ 726 - 9025) = \sqrt{1701} = 41.2432$$
Standard deviation of $y = \sqrt{(14\ 000/8 - (280/8)^2)}$
$$= \sqrt{(1750 - 1225)} = \sqrt{525} = 22.9129$$

We can now calculate the correlation coefficient:

$$r = \frac{34\ 160 - 8 \times 95 \times 35}{8 \times 41.2432 \times 22.9129} = \frac{34\ 160 - 26\ 600}{7560.001} = \frac{7560}{7560.001} = 1.00$$

Since x and y are related by a simple equation in this case, we would expect a perfect correlation. The very slight difference between the numerator and the denominator is due to our calculating the standard deviations to only four decimal places.

Absenteeism v. temperature

The figures in the first two columns were given in Table 28. We first calculate the figures in the next three columns (x^2, y^2 and xy). If you have any wrong, re-check your arithmetic.

Absenteeism Y	Temperature X	Y × Y	X × X	X × Y
3.90	26.00	15.21	676.00	101.40
2.70	17.00	7.29	289.00	45.90
3.00	23.00	9.00	529.00	69.00
3.10	25.00	9.61	625.00	77.50
2.60	21.00	6.76	441.00	54.60
4.00	28.00	16.00	784.00	112.00
2.80	22.00	7.84	484.00	61.60
3.80	27.00	14.44	729.00	102.60

We then sum each column and get the following results:

	Y	X	Y × Y	X × X	Y × X
Sum	25.90	189.00	86.15	4557.00	624.60

Now we calculate the mean of x and y:

  Mean of $x = 189/8 = 23.625$
  Mean of $y = 25.9/8 = 3.2375$

and the standard deviation of x and y:

Standard deviation of $x = \sqrt{(4557/8 - (189/8)^2)}$
$\qquad\qquad\qquad\qquad = \sqrt{(569.625 - 558.1406)} = 3.3889$
Standard deviation of $y = \sqrt{(86.15/8 - (25.9/8)^2)}$
$\qquad\qquad\qquad\qquad = \sqrt{(10.7687 - 10.4814)} = 0.536$

We can now calculate the correlation coefficient:

$$r = \frac{624.6 - 8 \times 23.625 \times 3.2375}{8 \times 3.3889 \times 0.536} = \frac{624.6 - 611.8875}{14.5316} = \frac{12.7125}{14.5316}$$

or:

$\qquad r = 0.8748$

Note that we have a fairly good positive correlation, which is what the scatter graph would lead us to expect.

■ CHAPTER 7   REGRESSION

Note: In calculating regression equations it is essential that you work to as many decimal places as possible in the calculations. The following results are given to four decimal places but all calculations have been done to six places.

Exercise 34   Regression equation of degrees Celsius v. degrees Fahrenheit

The figures in the first two columns were given in Table 32. We first calculate the figures in columns four and five (x^2, xy), and y^2 if using method 3. If you have any wrong, re-check your arithmetic.

Celsius Y	Fahrenheit X	Y × Y	X × X	X × Y
0	32	0	1 024	0
10	50	100	2 500	500
20	68	400	4 624	1 360
30	86	900	7 396	2 580
40	104	1 600	10 816	4 160
50	122	2 500	14 884	6 100
60	140	3 600	19 600	8 400
70	158	4 900	24 964	11 060

We then sum each column and get the following results:

	Y	X	Y × Y	X × X	Y × X
Sum	280	760	14 000	85 808	34 160

Method 1
Substituting in the equations:

$\qquad \Sigma y = nb + a\Sigma x$
and $\quad \Sigma xy = b\Sigma x + a\Sigma x^2$

We get:

$$280 = 8b + 760a \qquad (1)$$
$$\text{and} \quad 34\ 160 = 760b + 85\ 808a \qquad (2)$$

Multiplying the first equation by 760 and the second by 8, we get:

$$212\ 800 = 6\ 080b + 577\ 600a \qquad (3)$$
$$\text{and} \quad 273\ 280 = 6\ 080b + 686\ 464a \qquad (4)$$

Subtracting equation (3) from equation (4), we get:

$$60\ 480 = 108\ 864a$$
$$\therefore \quad a = 0.5556$$

Substituting this in equation (1), we get:

$$280 = 8b + 422.2222$$
$$\therefore \quad b = (280 - 422.2222)/8 = -17.7778$$

The regression equation is:

$$y = 0.5556x - 17.7778$$

Method 2
Substituting in the equations:

$$a = \frac{n\Sigma xy - (\Sigma x)(\Sigma y)}{n\Sigma x^2 - (\Sigma x)^2}$$

$$b = \frac{(\Sigma x)(\Sigma xy) - (\Sigma y)(\Sigma x^2)}{(\Sigma x)^2 - n\Sigma x^2}$$

we get:

$$a = \frac{8 \times 34\ 160 - 280 \times 760}{8 \times 85\ 808 - 760 \times 760} = \frac{60\ 480}{108\ 864} = 0.5556$$

and

$$b = \frac{760 \times 34\ 160 - 280 \times 85\ 808}{760 \times 760 - 8 \times 85\ 808} = \frac{-1\ 935\ 360}{108\ 864} = -17.7778$$

Method 3
We have already calculated the mean of x and y:

Mean of $x = 760/8 = 95.00$
Mean of $y = 280/8 = 35.00$

and the standard deviation of x and y:

Standard deviation of $x = 41.2432$
Standard deviation of $y = 22.9129$

and the correlation coefficient:

$$r = 1.00$$

Substituting in the equations:

$$a = \frac{r\sigma_y}{\sigma_x}$$

$$b = \bar{y} - a\bar{x}$$

we get:

$$a = \frac{1 \times 22.9129}{41.2432} = 0.5556$$

and

$$b = 35 - 0.5556 \times 95 = -17.7778$$

Exercise 35   Absenteeism v. temperature

The figures in the first two columns were given in Table 33. We first calculate the figures in the next three columns (x^2, y^2 and xy). If you have any wrong, re-check your arithmetic.

Absenteeism Y	Temperature X	$Y \times Y$	$X \times X$	$X \times Y$
3.90	26.00	15.21	676.00	101.40
2.70	17.00	7.29	289.00	45.90
3.00	23.00	9.00	529.00	69.00
3.10	25.00	9.61	625.00	77.50
2.60	21.00	6.76	441.00	54.60
4.00	28.00	16.00	784.00	112.00
2.80	22.00	7.84	484.00	61.60
3.80	27.00	14.44	729.00	102.60

We then sum each column and get the following results:

	Y	X	$Y \times Y$	$X \times X$	$Y \times X$
Sum	25.90	189.00	86.15	4557.00	624.60

Method 1
Substituting in the equations:

$$\Sigma y = nb + a\Sigma x$$
$$\text{and} \quad \Sigma xy = b\Sigma x + a\Sigma x^2$$

we get:

$$25.9 = 8b + 189a \tag{1}$$
$$\text{and} \quad 624.6 = 189b + 4577a \tag{2}$$

Multiplying equation (1) by 189 and equation (2) by 8 we get:

$$4895.1 = 1512b + 35\,721a \tag{3}$$
$$\text{and} \quad 4996.8 = 1512b + 36\,456a \tag{4}$$

Subtracting equation (3) from equation (4), we get:

$$101.7 = 735a$$
$$\therefore \quad a = 0.1384$$

Substituting this in equation (1), we get:

$$25.9 = 8b + 26.1576$$
$$\therefore \quad b = (25.9 - 26.1576)/8 = -0.0314$$

The regression equation is:

$$y = 0.1384x - 0.0322$$

Method 2

Substituting in the equations:

$$a = \frac{n\Sigma xy - (\Sigma x)(\Sigma y)}{n\Sigma x^2 - (\Sigma x)^2}$$

$$b = \frac{(\Sigma x)(\Sigma xy) - (\Sigma y)(\Sigma x^2)}{(\Sigma x)^2 - n\Sigma x^2}$$

we get:

$$a = \frac{8 \times 624.6 - 25.9 \times 189}{8 \times 4557 - 189 \times 189} = \frac{101.7}{735} = 0.1384$$

and

$$b = \frac{189 \times 624.6 - 25.9 \times 4557}{189 \times 189 - 8 \times 4557} = \frac{23.1}{-735} = -0.0314$$

Method 3

We have already calculated the mean of x and y:

Mean of $x = 189/8 = 23.625$
Mean of $y = 25.9/8 = 3.2375$

and the standard deviation of x and y:

Standard deviation of $x = 3.3889$
Standard deviation of $y = 0.536$

and the correlation coefficient:

$$r = 0.8748$$

Substituting in the equations:

$$a = \frac{r\sigma_y}{\sigma_x}$$
$$b = \bar{y} - a\bar{x}$$

we get:

$$a = 0.8748 \times 0.536/3.3889 = 0.1384$$

and

$$b = 3.2375 - 23.625 \times 0.1384 = -0.0313$$

■ CHAPTER 8   SAMPLING

Exercise 36   Standard error

The sample size is 1/10th of 500 = 50.
   The standard error = $\sigma/\sqrt{N} = 0.02/\sqrt{50} = 0.0028$.
   Note that the mean is not relevant to the question.

Exercise 37   Confidence interval

We are concerned about both ends of the distribution here, so the 95 per cent confidence interval is that interval which allows a 2.5 per cent probability at either extreme. Looking up 0.025 in the normal tables we get a z of 1.96, so the 95 per cent confidence interval is:

$$\bar{x} \pm 1.96 \times \text{standard error}$$

We know from Exercise 36 that $\bar{x}$ is 1.021 and the standard error is 0.0028 so the 95 per cent confidence interval is:

$$1.021 \pm 1.96 \times 0.0028 = 1.0155 \text{ to } 1.0265$$

If we had taken every fifth bag instead of every tenth, then the sample size would be 100 and the standard error $0.02/\sqrt{100}$ or 0.002. Assuming the sample mean remained the same, the 95 per cent confidence interval is now:

$$1.021 \pm 1.96 \times 0.002 = 1.017 \text{ to } 1.025$$

Exercise 38   Confidence interval using the *t*-distribution

Our sample size here is 500/20 = 25, so we must use the t-distribution, not the normal distribution. In addition, the standard deviation is a sample standard deviation on a small sample so we must apply the Bessel correction:

$$\sigma = s/\sqrt{N/(N-1)} = 0.02/\sqrt{25/24} = 0.0196$$

and the standard error is:

$$0.0196/\sqrt{25} = 0.00392$$

Looking up 24 degrees of freedom in the t-distribution, we find that the value of t for a probability of 5 per cent is 2.06, so the 95 per cent confidence interval is:

$$1.021 \pm 2.06 \times 0.00392 = 1.013 \text{ to } 1.029$$

This is quite a lot wider than the interval found in Exercise 37 of 1.0155 to 1.0265. The different is partly due to the larger standard error caused by the small sample and the Bessel correction, and partly due to the flatter t-distribution. This illustrates the general principle that the more information we have, the more precise our answer can be.

Exercise 39   Binomial standard error

The 95 per cent confidence interval is $P \pm 2\sqrt{PQ/N}$.
   In the case of brand A:

$$P = 37, Q = 100 - 37 = 63, N = 1024$$

so the interval is:

$$37 \pm 2\sqrt{37 \times 63/1024} = 37 \pm 3.02$$

   In the case of brand B:

$$P = 34, Q = 66, N = 1024$$

so the interval is:

$$34 \pm 2\sqrt{34 \times 66/1024} = 34 \pm 2.96$$

   It is noteworthy that despite the large sample, the error is still about ± 10 per cent of the mean.

Exercise 40   Sampling social security records

One way of taking a true random sample would be to take four-digit numbers from a random number table. We would ignore any numbers above 3000, those below 3000 would select records. We would first have to number the records consecutively. Once 150 records had been selected, the process would stop.

   This is a time-consuming process and what is more likely to happen is that we would take every $3000/150 = 20$th record, having used random number tables to pick a number between 1 and 20 as our starting point. This involves far less work in identifying the sample and far less work in selecting them since the process is sequential, i.e. we go from one end of the files to the other.

■ CHAPTER 9   TESTS OF SIGNIFICANCE

Exercise 41   Effect of sales training

We have $\mu = 145$ $\sigma = 40$
              $\bar{x} = 130$ $N = 100$

   The hypotheses are:

H_0: $\bar{x} = \mu$
H_1: $\bar{x} <> \mu$

In other words, we are only interested in change in effectiveness, not the direction of change.

   Since we are looking at means and $N > 30$ we use the z-test, and the critical values of z at the 5 per cent significance level are ± 1.96.

   The standard error is $40/\sqrt{100} = 4$.

   The critical values are therefore $145 \pm 1.96 \times 4 = 137.16$ and 152.84. Since $\bar{x}$ lies outside that range, we reject H_0 and accept H_1.

Exercise 42 Effect of advertising

We have $\mu = 145$ $\quad \sigma = 40$
$\quad\quad\quad\quad\bar{x} = 160$ $\quad N = 100$

The hypotheses are:

H_0: $\quad \bar{x} \leqslant \mu$
H_1: $\quad \bar{x} > \mu$

Here we are concerned with $\bar{x}$ being greater than μ and the hypotheses reflect this.

The standard error is $40/\sqrt{100} = 4$.

The critical value of z is (5 per cent level of significance, one tail) 1.645, therefore the critical value for $\bar{x}$ is $145 + 1.645 \times 4 = 151.58$.

We therefore reject H_0 and accept H_1.

Exercise 43 Effect of training on productivity

We have

	$\bar{x}$	s
Trained	435	44
Untrained	410	48
N	12	12

H_0: $\bar{x}_1 = \bar{x}_2$
H_1: $\bar{x}_1 <> \bar{x}_2$

With two small samples we must use the t-test and:

$$t = \frac{\bar{x}_1 - \bar{x}_2}{\sqrt{(s_1{}^2 + s_2{}^2)/(N - 1)}}$$

$$= \frac{435 - 410}{\sqrt{(44^2 + 48^2)/11}}$$

$$= 1.273$$

We have $(2N - 2) = 22$ degrees of freedom and the critical value of t at 5 per cent significance is 2.07. Our value is less than this so we cannot reject H_0. We cannot conclude that the scheme has made no difference, but we have failed to find evidence for a difference.

Exercise 44 Difference in standard deviation

Their means are irrelevant. We have:

$\sigma = 40$ $\quad\quad s = 60$ $\quad\quad N = 100$

H_0: $\quad \sigma = s$
H_1: $\quad \sigma <> s$

Comparing a sample standard deviation with a population standard deviation is a

z-test and:

$$z = (s - \sigma)/(\sigma/\sqrt{2 \times N})$$
$$= (60 - 40)/(40\sqrt{200})$$
$$= 7.07$$

The critical value of z at 5 per cent significance is 1.96. Since our calculated value is greater than this, we must reject H_0 and conclude that the standard deviation has changed.

Exercise 45   Consistency of life expectancy

We have:

Supplier	$\bar{x}$	s	N
A	124	18	17
B	121	12	20

H_0: $s_B \geqslant s_A$
H_1: $s_B < s_A$

This is a variance ratio or F-test:

$$F = s_A{}^2/s_B{}^2 = 18^2/12^2 = 2.25$$

The degrees of freedom are $(17 - 1) = 16$ and $(20 - 1) = 19$, for the larger and smaller variances respectively. Entering the tables we find a critical value of F at the 5 per cent significance level of 2.21.

Our value is greater than this so we may reject H_0 and conclude that supplier B does supply a superior product.

Exercise 46   Opinion of holiday resorts

The initial position is:

Satisfaction Resort	1	2	3	4	Sum
A	10	55	74	30	169
B	35	30	24	5	94
C	20	44	30	2	96
Sum	65	129	128	37	359

First we calculate the expected values, on the basis of the null hypothesis that there is no difference between the resorts:

Satisfaction Resort	1	2	3	4	Sum
A	30.6	60.7	60.3	17.4	169.0
B	17.0	33.8	33.5	9.7	94.0
C	17.4	34.5	34.2	9.9	96.0
Sum	65.0	129.0	128.0	37.0	359.0

Then we calculate $O - E$:

Satisfaction Resort	1	2	3	4
A	−20.6	−5.7	13.7	12.6
B	18.0	−3.8	−9.5	−4.7
C	2.6	9.5	−4.2	−7.9

Then $(O - E)^2/E$:

Satisfaction Resort	1	2	3	4
A	13.9	0.5	3.1	9.1
B	19.0	0.4	2.7	2.3
C	0.4	2.6	0.5	6.3

Summing this table we have $\chi^2 = 60.85$.

We have $(3 - 1)(4 - 1) = 6$ degrees of freedom, and the critical value of χ^2 at 5 per cent significance and 6 degrees of freedom is 12.59. Our value is much greater so we reject H_0 and conclude that there is a difference between the resorts.

Exercise 47   Significance of the correlation coefficient

We have:

$$r = 0.8784 \qquad N = 8$$
H_0:   The correlation arose by chance.

$$t = r\sqrt{(N - 2)}/\sqrt{(1 - r^2)}$$
$$= 0.8784 \times \sqrt{6}/\sqrt{(1 - 0.8784^2)}$$
$$= 4.5$$

We have $(8 - 2) = 6$ degrees of freedom, and at the 5 per cent significance level the critical value of t is 2.45. Since the calculated value is greater than this we reject H_0 and accept that the correlation coefficient did not arise by chance.

At the 1 per cent level, the critical value of t is 3.71, so we still reject H_0, but we would not reject H_0 at the 0.1 per cent level.

■ CHAPTER 10   INDEX NUMBERS

Exercise 48   Indices for Company X sales

The sales are:
1986	360
1987	369
1988	390

With 1988 as the base, the indices are:

1986	$360 \times 100/390 = 92.3$
1987	$369 \times 100/390 = 94.6$

Exercise 49   Laspeyres and Paasche indices

The Laspeyres index uses the base year quantities as fixed weights, so we can ignore subsequent year quantities. The following table shows the calculation. First we multiply each year's prices by the 1985 quantities and sum these products for each year. We then index these sums by dividing by the 1985 sum and multiplying by 100.

Product	Price	1985 Qty	Qty × price	1986 Price	Qty × price	1987 Price	Qty × price
A	9.5	11.0	104.50	9.8	107.80	11.3	124.30
B	2.7	15.5	41.85	3.2	49.60	3.4	52.70
C	4.4	27.0	118.80	4.5	121.50	4.1	110.70
D	8.4	2.1	17.64	7.0	14.70	6.5	13.65
Sum			282.79		293.60		301.35
Index			100.00		103.82		106.56

The Paasche index uses current weights so we multiply current price by current quantity and sum these products for each year. We also need to multiply original price by current quantity to obtain the current base. The indices are calculated by dividing the current by the base total and multiplying by 100.

Product	1985 Price	1986 Price	Qty	Price × qty	1987 Price	Qty	Price × qty
A	9.5	9.8	12.4	121.52	11.3	10.2	115.26
B	2.7	3.2	17.8	56.96	3.4	22.1	75.14
C	4.4	4.5	18.0	81.00	4.1	11.2	45.92
D	8.4	7.0	12.0	84.00	6.5	17.5	113.75
Sum				343.48			350.07
Base totals							
A	9.5	9.5	12.4	117.80	9.5	10.2	96.90
B	2.7	2.7	17.8	48.06	2.7	22.1	59.67
C	4.4	4.4	18.0	79.20	4.4	11.2	49.28
D	8.4	8.4	12.0	100.80	8.4	17.5	147.00
				345.86			352.85
Index				99.31			99.21

It is worth noting that neither index reflects the rise in turnover due to the rapid increase in sales of product D.

■ CHAPTER 11   FORECASTING

Exercise 50   Three-month moving average

The easiest way to calculate a three-month moving average is simply to sum the first three figures and divide by three, then sum the second, third and fourth figures and divide by three, and so on. This is shown in the table:

Month	Sales	3-month average
Jan	7.5	
Feb	7.8	
Mar	6.3	7.20
Apr	8.2	7.43
May	7.0	7.17
Jun	7.0	7.40
Jul	6.4	6.80
Aug	6.7	6.70
Sep	6.3	6.47
Oct	4.5	5.83
Nov	5.9	5.57
Dec	6.2	5.53

If we were calculating a moving average for longer than three periods, the alternative, subtract the oldest value from the sum and add the newest, is worth considering, but with only three figures totalling each time is easier.

Exercise 51   Sales forecast for autumn 1988

We calculate the base sales for autumn 1988 by taking our last moving average of 237.25 and adding two trend values to compensate for the lag, and a further three to take us to autumn 1988 from winter 1987.

Base sales for autumn 1988 = $237.25 + 5 \times 4.13 = 257.90$.

We can now apply the autumn seasonal adjustment of -9.81 per cent which gives us a forecast of 232.6.

Exercise 52   Forecast demand for first quarter of 1988

First we calculate the average trend as shown below:

Year	Quarter	Sales	1-year average	Difference
1985	1	22		
	2	41		
	3	36		
	4	18	29.25	
1986	1	24	29.75	0.50
	2	53	32.75	3.00
	3	55	37.50	4.75
	4	27	39.75	2.25
1987	1	25	40.00	0.25
	2	60	41.75	1.75
	3	52	41.00	−0.75
	4	32	42.45	1.25
Mean				1.63

Then we calculate the adjusted sales by removing the average trend, i.e. we subtract 1.63 from period 2, 3.26 from period 3 etc. Once we have done this we calculate the mean adjusted sales and calculate the seasonal factors from the formula:

$$\frac{(\text{Adjusted sales} - \text{Mean adjusted sales}) \times 100}{\text{Mean adjusted sales}}$$

This is shown in the following table:

Year	Quarter	Sales	Adjusted sales	Seasonal factors 1	2	3	4
1985	1	22	22.00	−21.76			
	2	41	39.37		40.01		
	3	36	32.74			16.43	
	4	18	13.11				−53.38
1986	1	24	17.48	−37.84			
	2	53	44.85		59.50		
	3	55	45.22			60.81	
	4	27	15.59				−44.56
1987	1	25	11.96	−57.47			
	2	60	45.33		61.20		
	3	52	35.70			26.96	
	4	32	14.70				−49.96
Mean			28.12	−39.02	53.57	34.73	−49.30

We now add two trend values to the last moving average to allow for the lag, a further value to bring us to the first quarter of 1988 which gives us $42.25 + 3 \times 1.63 = 47.14$.

We now make the seasonal adjustment of −39.02 per cent to get our forecast of 28.75.

Exercise 53 Exponential smoothing

The first problem is to establish an assumed forecast for the first period. Unless the figures show a marked seasonality, then the first sales figure is as good a starting point as any. (If there is marked seasonality, then a mean would be a better starting point, but we must then be careful to allow for any trend.)

Having chosen 7.50 as our forecast for January, we now substitute in the equation:

$$F_{t+1} = 0.1A_t + (1 - 0.1)F_t$$

The table shows the result:

Month	Sales	Forecast
Jan	7.50	7.50
Feb	7.80	7.53
Mar	6.30	7.41
Apr	8.20	7.49
May	7.00	7.44
Jun	7.00	7.39

Jul	6.40	7.29
Aug	6.70	7.24
Sep	6.30	7.14
Oct	4.50	6.88
Nov	5.90	6.78
Dec	6.20	6.72

Exercise 54   Forecasting by regression

First we need to construct the regression table as follows:

Year	Quarter (X)	Sales (Y)	X^2	Y^2	XY
1985	1	22	1	484	22
	2	41	4	1 681	82
	3	36	9	1 296	108
	4	18	16	324	72
1986	5	24	25	576	120
	6	53	36	2 809	318
	7	55	49	3 025	385
	8	27	64	729	216
1987	9	25	81	625	225
	10	60	100	3 600	600
	11	52	121	2 704	572
	12	32	144	1 024	384
Sum	78	445	650	18 877	3104
Mean	6.50	37.08			

Using whichever method you choose, calculate the regression constants a and b. You will find:

$$a =   1.48$$
$$b = 27.47$$

With a trend of 1.48 per period, we can now adjust the sales figures for trend and extract the seasonal factors as in Exercise 52.

Year	Quarter (X)	Sales (Y)	Adjusted sales	Seasonal factors 1	2	3	4
1985	1	22	22.00	−23.98			
	2	41	39.52		36.56		
	3	36	33.04			14.17	
	4	18	13.56				−53.14
1986	5	24	18.08	−37.53			
	6	53	45.60		57.57		
	7	55	46.12			59.36	
	8	27	16.64				−42.50
1987	9	25	13.16	−54.53			
	10	60	46.68		61.30		
	11	52	37.20			28.54	
	12	32	15.72				−45.68
Mean			28.94	−38.68	51.81	34.02	−47.11

We can now forecast the sales for quarter 1, 1988. We use the regression equation:

Sales = 1.48 × period + 27.47

to forecast the base sales of 1.48 × 13 + 27.47 = 46.70, and then apply the seasonal correction of −38.68 per cent to get a forecast of 28.64.

In Exercise 52 we obtained a forecast of 28.75. The agreement between the two methods is remarkably good. The seasonal factors calculated by the two methods are very close, but the difference between the trends will become more important as we try to forecast further into the future. Since all forecasting methods become more unreliable as we try to forecast further into the future, this need not really concern us.

■ CHAPTER 12   STATISTICAL QUALITY CONTROL

Exercise 55   Operating characteristic of a 1000, 100, 0 scheme

The following table shows the proportion of batches accepted for various levels of actual defectives:

1000, 100, 0 scheme

Actual % *defectives*	*Mean* *(np)*	*P*(0)
0.00	0.00	1.00
1.00	1.00	0.37
2.50	2.50	0.08
5.00	5.00	0.01
7.50	7.50	0.00
10.00	10.00	0.00
20.00	20.00	0.00

These figures are exactly the same as those in Table 56.

The characteristic is plotted in Fig. 72, with the 1000, 100, 4 characteristic for comparison. It is obvious that, while passing very few defective batches, the scheme shows even poorer discrimination. This is a characteristics of all N, n, 0 schemes.

Exercise 56   Action and warning limits

The mean = np = 20 × 0.15 = 3.0.

The standard deviation = $\sqrt{npq}$ = $\sqrt{20 \times 0.15 \times 0.85}$ = 1.60.

The warning limits are ±2σ = ±3.2 and the action limits are ±3σ = ±4.8.

This means that both lower limits are in fact below 0 and can be ignored. The upper limits are:

Warning: 3 + 3.2 = 6.2
Action: 3 + 4.8 = 7.8

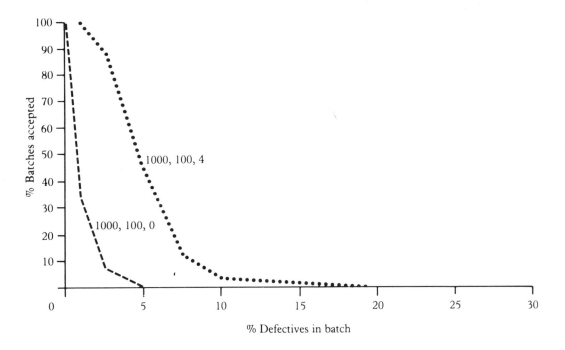

Fig. 72   Operating characteristic 1000, 100, 0

Appendix 3   Table of the normal distribution

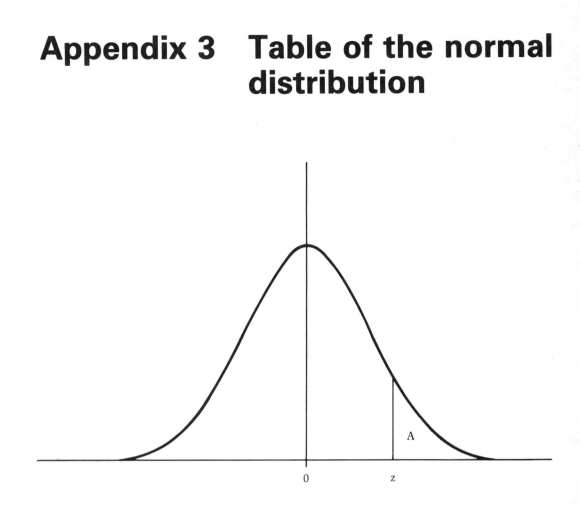

Fig. 73

$z = (x - \mu)/\sigma$ A is the area to the right of z

z	A	z	A	z	A
0.00	0.5000	1.00	0.1587	2.00	0.0228
0.05	0.4801	1.05	0.1469	2.05	0.0202
0.10	0.4602	1.10	0.1357	2.10	0.0179
0.15	0.4404	1.15	0.1251	2.15	0.0158
0.20	0.4207	1.20	0.1151	2.20	0.0139
0.25	0.4013	1.25	0.1057	2.25	0.0122
0.30	0.3821	1.30	0.0968	2.30	0.0107
0.35	0.3632	1.35	0.0885	2.35	0.0094
0.40	0.3446	1.40	0.0808	2.40	0.0082
0.45	0.3264	1.45	0.0735	2.45	0.0071
0.50	0.3085	1.50	0.0668	2.50	0.0062
0.55	0.2912	1.55	0.0606	2.55	0.0054
0.60	0.2743	1.60	0.0548	2.60	0.0047
0.65	0.2575	1.65	0.0495	2.65	0.0040
0.70	0.2420	1.70	0.0446	2.70	0.0035
0.75	0.2267	1.75	0.0406	2.75	0.0030
0.80	0.2119	1.80	0.0359	2.80	0.0026
0.85	0.1977	1.85	0.0322	2.85	0.0022
0.90	0.1841	1.90	0.0287	2.90	0.0019
0.95	0.1711	1.95	0.0256	2.95	0.0016

z	A
3.00	0.00135
3.10	0.00097
3.20	0.00069
3.30	0.00048
3.40	0.00034
3.50	0.00023
3.75	0.00009
4.00	0.00003

Appendix 4   Table of the *t*-distribution

Degrees of freedom	Probability			
	5%	2%	1%	0.1%
1	12.71	31.82	63.66	636.62
2	4.30	6.97	9.93	31.60
3	3.18	4.54	5.84	12.94
4	2.78	3.75	4.61	8.61
5	2.57	3.37	4.03	6.86
6	2.45	3.14	3.71	5.96
7	2.37	3.00	3.50·	5.41
8	2.31	2.90	3.36	5.04
9	2.26	2.82	3.25	4.78
10	2.23	2.76	3.17	4.59
11	2.20	2.72	3.11	4.44
12	2.18	2.68	3.06	4.32
13	2.16	2.65	3.01	4.22
14	2.15	2.62	2.98	4.14
15	2.13	2.60	2.95	4.07
16	2.12	2.58	2.92	4.02
17	2.11	2.57	2.00	3.97
18	2.10	2.55	2.88	3.92
19	2.09	2.54	2.86	3.88
20	2.09	2.53	2.85	3.85
21	2.08	2.52	2.83	3.82
22	2.07	2.51	2.82	3.79
23	2.07	2.50	2.81	3.77
24	2.06	2.49	2.80	3.75
25	2.06	2.49	2.79	3.73
26	2.06	2.48	2.78	3.71
27	2.05	2.47	2.77	3.69
28	2.05	2.47	2.76	3.67
29	2.05	2.46	2.76	3.66
30	2.04	2.46	2.75	3.65
∞	1.96	2.33	2.58	3.29

Note: For a one-tailed test, halve the probability.

Appendix 5 Table of the *F*-distribution

Note: This table gives the values for the 5 per cent level of significance only.

Smaller variance	Degrees of freedom of larger variance				
	1	2	3	4	5
1	161.40	199.50	215.70	224.60	230.20
2	18.50	19.00	19.20	19.20	19.30
3	10.13	9.55	9.28	9.12	9.01
4	7.71	6.94	6.59	6.39	6.26
5	6.61	5.79	5.41	5.19	5.05
6	5.99	5.14	4.76	4.53	4.39
7	5.59	4.74	4.35	4.12	3.97
8	5.32	4.46	4.07	3.84	3.69
9	5.12	4.26	3.86	3.63	3.48
10	4.96	4.10	3.71	3.48	3.33
11	4.84	3.98	3.59	3.36	3.20
12	4.75	3.89	3.49	3.26	3.11
13	4.67	3.81	3.41	3.18	3.03
14	4.60	3.74	3.34	3.11	2.96
15	4.54	3.68	3.29	3.06	2.90
20	4.35	3.49	3.10	2.90	2.71
25	4.24	3.39	2.99	2.76	2.60
30	4.17	3.32	2.92	2.69	2.53
∞	3.84	3.00	2.60	2.37	2.21

Smaller variance	Degrees of freedom of larger variance				
	7	10	20	30	∞
1	236.80	241.90	248.00	250.10	254.30
2	19.40	19.40	19.45	19.46	19.50
3	8.89	8.79	8.66	8.62	8.53
4	6.09	5.96	5.80	5.75	5.63
5	4.88	4.74	4.56	4.50	4.36
6	4.21	4.06	3.87	3.81	3.67
7	3.79	3.64	3.44	3.38	3.23
8	3.50	3.35	3.15	3.08	2.93
9	3.29	3.14	2.94	2.86	2.71
10	3.14	2.98	2.77	2.70	2.54
11	3.01	2.85	2.65	2.57	2.40
12	2.91	2.75	2.54	2.46	2.30
13	2.83	2.67	2.46	2.38	2.21
14	2.76	2.60	2.39	2.31	2.13
15	2.71	2.54	2.33	2.25	2.07
20	2.51	2.35	2.12	2.04	1.84
25	2.40	2.24	2.00	1.92	1.71
30	2.33	2.16	1.93	1.84	1.62
∞	2.01	1.83	1.57	1.46	1.00

Appendix 6   Table of the χ^2-distribution

Degrees of freedom	Significance level	
	5%	1%
1	3.84	6.63
2	5.99	9.21
3	7.81	11.34
4	9.49	13.28
5	11.07	15.09
6	12.59	16.81
7	14.07	18.48
8	15.51	20.09
9	16.92	21.67
10	18.31	23.21
11	19.68	24.73
12	21.03	26.22
13	22.36	27.69
14	23.68	29.14
15	25.00	30.58
16	26.30	32.00
17	27.59	33.41
18	28.87	34.81
19	30.14	36.19
20	31.41	37.57
25	37.65	44.31
30	43.77	50.89

Appendix 7 Table of random numbers

94	79	98	30	90	98	47	62	47	45	24
2	96	95	12	30	97	34	34	77	89	96
23	46	59	7	82	93	45	34	96	44	81
64	58	7	56	86	3	25	14	79	78	62
26	90	46	87	89	53	89	100	26	95	27
4	86	71	16	52	24	94	21	53	59	85
22	64	76	99	92	68	60	16	54	58	37
54	36	42	93	72	34	27	75	35	66	31
72	86	5	94	7	79	89	66	58	8	25
8	41	97	71	90	70	3	89	6	60	82
57	47	18	85	54	35	17	38	12	42	75
65	45	78	29	73	43	84	87	98	85	70
38	87	21	21	37	25	15	32	41	5	6
85	83	61	20	30	78	23	1	60	37	97
41	60	43	99	77	59	12	44	96	89	94
82	94	84	53	86	50	61	45	100	68	13
19	21	65	49	91	55	94	64	56	84	67
75	25	58	49	5	29	29	67	41	57	11
69	30	11	27	34	92	86	96	39	53	5
97	91	30	40	93	14	41	35	76	76	87

Index